STARTING OUT WITH BEES

For Debbie & Keith
With best wishes
John Williams   6/March 2012

STARTING OUT WITH BEES

John Williams

BeeCraft

A catalogue record for this book is available from the British Library.

ISBN 978–0–900147–09–8

Published in Great Britain by
Bee Craft Limited
The National Beekeeping Centre
National Agricultural Centre
Stoneleigh Park
Warwickshire
CV8 2LG

www.bee-craft.com

Typeset by Alex Ellis

Printed in Great Britain by Cambrian Printers, Aberystwyth

Acknowledgements
There are many people who have helped me write this book and I am pleased to acknowledge that without their help the book would probably not have been produced.

Towards the end of 2008 I was asked by Claire Waring, the editor of *Bee Craft*, to write the monthly articles for beginners during 2009. The articles under the title 'Starting Out' were completed with patient help and guidance from Margaret Cowley. Andrew Gibb suggested that the articles could be the basis of a book for beginners to be published by Bee Craft Limited.

I also thank some of the many people who have helped me to learn how to keep bees. Nick Withers was my mentor when I started with bees and he has helped me over many years. Nick has made many helpful suggestions and provided some of the photographs for the book. Brian Palmer was the County Beekeeping Instructor in Kent in the 1980s. Margaret Thomas was my tutor on the BBKA correspondence course for some of the modules. I am grateful too for the friendship and help with bees from members of the Westerham Branch of the Kent Beekeepers' Association.

Picture Credits
I want to thank the following for allowing me to use their photographs: Crown Copyright, Food and Environment Agency, National Bee Unit; Claire Waring; Margaret Cowley; Nick Withers; Geoff Close; Chris Jackson. The illustration (p11) is adapted with the kind permission of Clive de Bruyn from an original illustration by Keta de Bruyn. The illustration (p19) is based on a photograph by Nick Withers, drawn by Alex Ellis.

The following kindly allowed me to take photographs in their apiaries: Carol and Edwin Taylor (front cover), Orpington Apiary Club (p13), Jane and Adam Skinner (p16).

CONTENTS

INTRODUCTION

This book is based on my own experience keeping bees on the North Downs near the borders of Kent, Surrey and Greater London. What bees are up to depends on the time of the year and the weather, so at any particular time there is quite a wide variation in the bees' behaviour throughout the British Isles. So what we must do to care for our bees month by month depends on the bees' needs, which may not follow exactly the calendar of bees' activities and beekeepers' jobs set out in this book.

Some of you may have started with bees already and you may have one or perhaps two or three colonies. Others may be beginning to explore how to get started. The focus of this book is on the practical aspects of beekeeping and what you need to do month by month when starting out with bees. I have described briefly what the bees are likely to be doing in the colony each month so that you can link the beekeeping tasks to the needs of the bees. I have started the month-by-month account of the bees' activities and how the beekeeper can help in August. This is when the beekeeping year really begins with the preparations for winter.

I trust that the details about stings in Chapter 1 do not put you off beekeeping before you start. However, if you are one of the few people who may suffer a serious reaction you need to know about stings and sadly it may be that beekeeping is not for you. I would reassure anyone who is simply apprehensive to persevere. After a little experience stings are not a big issue for most beekeepers.

Chapter 6 is about bee health matters and includes an introduction to disabilities and diseases. Like all livestock bees do sometimes suffer from disease and to care for your bees you need to know when you need to ask for advice. As with stings, I trust that you will not be put off beekeeping because of the many problems that can affect our bees. It can be very discouraging if you are unlucky and experience a serious problem in your first year or two. Most beekeepers will find common diseases such as nosema and chalk brood some time and varroa all the time, but many beekeepers rarely experience the really serious notifiable diseases.

Some aspects of the bee's behaviour are described but not explained in detail. When you have mastered the basics you will probably want to study bee anatomy, biology and social life in more detail as well as more advanced beekeeping methods. There is a list of recommended books for further study in Appendix 3.

1 THE HONEY BEE COLONY

A normal colony in winter comprises a single queen and some 10 to 15,000 worker bees. In summer the colony will grow to 40 to 50,000 workers with a single queen and a few hundred male bees known as drones.

The queen is female and mates with several drones during one to three mating flights between five and 20 days after emerging from her cell. She stores sperm in an organ called a 'spermatheca' and lays fertilised eggs in the hexagonal beeswax cells to produce worker bees and unfertilised eggs in the slightly larger cells to produce drones, the male bees. The queen herself comes from a fertilised egg laid in a queen cell, a vertical cylindrical tapered cell built on the honeycomb. The larva develops into a queen because it is fed with a richer diet than the food for worker larvae. The queen lays all the eggs, maintains colony cohesion and influences colony activities through pheromones produced in her glands. This pheromone, called queen substance, suppresses the development of workers' ovaries and prevents the workers laying eggs and making swarm preparations. The queen uses her sting only on other queens in the hive.

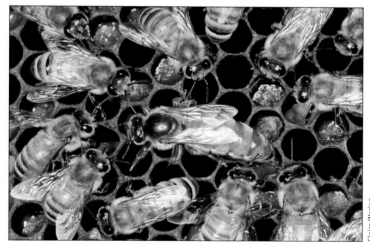

The queen bee lays eggs and maintains colony cohesion through pheromones

Claire Waring

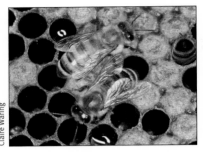

Claire Waring

The worker bees do all the necessary work, except egg-laying, to maintain colony wellbeing

Claire Waring

The drones have large eyes and strong wing muscles. Their main function is to mate with the queen

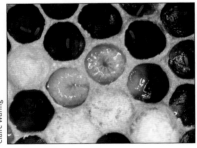

Claire Waring

Eggs hatch in three days. Larvae lie in 'c' shape in the cell, and are pearly white with visible segments

Workers are female bees with underdeveloped ovaries and are unable to mate. The workers do all the work necessary to maintain the wellbeing of the colony except egg production. As soon as they emerge as adults, for about three weeks they do all the 'housework'. The workers tend to carry out tasks related to age, starting with cleaning cells, and then feeding larvae, receiving nectar, pollen, water and propolis from foragers, processing nectar, ventilating the hive by fanning, producing wax, building cells and guarding the entrance. Other tasks include regulating temperature and humidity, removing debris and corpses and defending the colony, using their barbed sting. The worker bee in summer will spend the remaining three weeks or so of her life foraging.

Drones are male bees and their main task is to mate with the queen. After mating they die and the majority who do not mate are evicted from the colony, usually in August, and they too die. Drones do not have a sting mechanism.

The eggs hatch into larvae three days after being laid. The larvae are fed by nurse bees for five days for a queen, six days for a worker and seven days for a drone. The cell is then sealed, that is capped by wax; the larva changes into a pupa then into an adult bee and emerges from the cell 16 days after the egg was laid for a queen, 21 days for a worker and 24 days for a drone.

From egg to adult	Queen	Worker	Drone
Eggs hatch on day	3	3	3
Cell sealed on day	8	9	10
Adult emerges on day	16	21	24

Queens can live for up to five years but are usually replaced after two or three years by the bees. Good beekeeping practice is to replace the queen after two years. Workers live for about six weeks in summer and six months in winter.

THE INDIVIDUAL BEE

The body of the bee, like all insects, is made up of three main parts, the head, the thorax and the abdomen.

The head carries a pair of antennae covered with sensory endings for touch, taste and smell, the eyes and mouth parts. The brain and several glands are inside the head.

The thorax supports the three pairs of legs and two pairs of wings. It contains the large flight muscles, which generate heat both in flight and at rest to maintain body temperature.

The abdomen is attached to the thorax and contains the heart, gut, malpighian tubules that function as a kidney, and reproductive organs. The queen and workers have a sting mechanism and glands, and workers also have wax glands. The queen's abdomen contains the spermatheca to store male sperm.

External anatomy of a worker honey bee

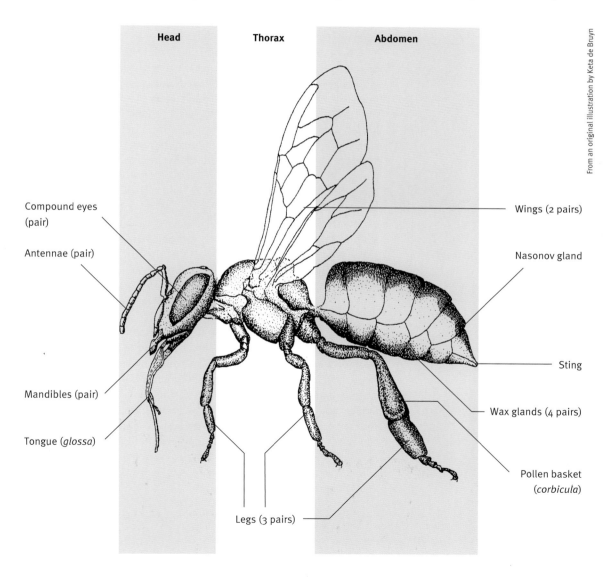

Head   Thorax   Abdomen

Compound eyes (pair)

Antennae (pair)

Mandibles (pair)

Tongue (*glossa*)

Wings (2 pairs)

Nasonov gland

Sting

Wax glands (4 pairs)

Pollen basket (*corbicula*)

Legs (3 pairs)

From an original illustration by Keta de Bruyn

STINGS

Many people attracted to beekeeping, and beginners, are understandably concerned about stings. When stung most people will feel some pain lasting less than 30 seconds followed by localised swelling, and the sting area may be red, itchy and tender for a couple of days. As a beginner you can expect to get the occasional sting but by learning to keep docile colonies and good handling methods you will find that there will be fewer stings. Most beekeepers get accustomed to stings and suffer little or no swelling and tenderness afterwards.

The worker bee uses her sting to defend the colony as a last resort. The sting mechanism is made up of two barbed lancets that are supported by moving plates and muscles. The lancets move forward alternately to penetrate the tissue of the intruder. When the barb is inserted in the tough elastic human skin the bee tears herself away leaving the sting mechanism, including the muscles and venom sac, behind. The injured bee will die within a few hours. The venom will continue to be pumped into the wound and it sends a chemical signal to alert other workers to come and sting. So the quicker the sting is removed the less venom will be injected.

The best way to reduce the effect of the sting is to remove the sting as quickly as possible by scraping the sting mechanism away using your finger nail or the edge of your hive tool. Try to avoid grasping the barb between your fingers to pull it out as this may result in more venom being squeezed into the wound. The sting site may be rubbed with some grass, or cool smoke used to reduce the effect of the alarm signal.

A few people may suffer a more serious and uncomfortable reaction within a few minutes after being stung. This may involve nausea, wheezing, vomiting and a rash all over the body like a nettle rash. Some de-sensitising treatment is available but this group should consult their doctor before starting with beekeeping.

A small proportion of the population suffers a severe allergic reaction to stings and may experience an anaphylactic shock that can result in death if not treated quickly. If you do not know how you will react to stings make sure that you are with other people who know you do not know when you are near beehives such as at apiary demonstrations.

2 LEARNING TO KEEP BEES

The challenges brought about by new pests and diseases mean that all beekeepers, including experienced ones, need to carry on learning probably for as long as they keep bees. As a beginner you will want to learn the basics as quickly as possible. Later there will be plenty of opportunities to learn more about the biology, social life and behaviour of our wonderful and amazing honey bee.

Many beekeeping groups have a training apiary for beginners to gain practical experience with bees

Local beekeeping groups

It really is worth while joining a local group of beekeepers as soon as you can and before you start buying anything. In these local groups you will find enthusiastic and friendly people, some with a lot of experience, and a growing number of beginners too. Many groups have demonstration apiaries with special provision for beginners to experience handling bees and equipment. The programme of meetings may include winter lectures and summer demonstrations. Many groups help beginners by asking experienced beekeepers to act as mentors.

These groups have various names. They may be called Branches or Divisions of Area Associations in England. They are affiliated to the British Beekeepers' Association (BBKA). In Wales and the Republic of Ireland they are called Local Associations affiliated to the Welsh Beekeepers' Association (WBKA) or to the Federation of Irish Beekeeping Associations (FIBKA). In Northern Ireland the local groups are called clubs and they are affiliated to the Ulster Beekeepers' Association (UBKA). The Scottish Beekeepers' Association (SBA) represent beekeepers in Scotland. You can usually find details of your local group by contacting the appropriate Association.

Beginners' courses

There are basic training courses throughout the country arranged by individual experienced beekeepers or by some beekeeping groups. During the winter months many courses are classroom-based covering the basic syllabus in eight to ten weekly sessions. There are intensive weekend courses too. During the spring and summer there are courses covering the practical aspects, usually based in a training apiary. You can find out about courses arranged in your area from your local beekeeping group or by searching on the internet. *Bee Craft* usually publishes every year in January a list of courses in the *Bee Craft* Courses Directory.

Home study

Many beginners who are unable to find a suitable course nearby or at a convenient time enrol with the BBKA Correspondence Course. Some successfully study at home. If you are attending a course and especially if you are embarking on studying at home on your own, you will benefit by joining an informal discussion group. If you cannot find one in your area, perhaps you could start one based on your local group.

3 SELECTING THE APIARY SITE

It is worth while thinking carefully about where to place your hive because once the bees have settled it will not be easy to move the hive at short notice if required. Of course it is most important that the bees will have access to good forage. They depend on nectar and pollen and will forage up to two or three miles from the hive. There are advantages in keeping more than one colony and you may want to expand in future so it is worth thinking ahead and planning how you would accommodate some additional hives.

Most beginners like to keep their bees in the garden. This is fine if they can be placed well away from your house and patio and from the boundary with your neighbours. You must avoid the bees being a nuisance to your family, neighbours and passers-by.

The hives may be hidden from view and surrounded by some form of obstruction about two metres high so that the bees' flight path is above people's heads. A hedge is ideal, or one side of a shed, perhaps a shed to store beekeeping gear near the apiary. A fence or a fine screen of garden netting will also be suitable. Your neighbours have a right to use their entire garden including just the other side of the shared fence on warm summer afternoons perhaps wearing only shorts, when you might want to examine and manipulate your bees.

If your garden is too small, an 'out-apiary' is a good solution. A small corner of a field may be suitable. Your local association may have the names of people willing and sometimes enthusiastic to let a beekeeper use part of their land, large garden or orchard. Another possibility is to rent an allotment, but some allotment committees are not keen to allow beehives on their allotment after their experience with beekeepers that failed to control swarms or kept bad-tempered bees.

Here is a summary of what bees need to maintain colony health and to thrive:

- near to a variety of flowers for nectar and pollen
- shelter from wind
- good air drainage and no frost pockets
- space underneath the hive(s) for free air flow to prevent dampness persisting in winter
- irregular positioning of hives or entrances to reduce bees 'drifting' into neighbouring hives.

This is a summary of the features that you and your neighbours will want:

- good access for the beekeeper especially when carrying equipment and heavy supers
- hedge or other barrier around the apiary to raise bees' flight paths above people's heads
- plenty of space for the working area around each hive, such as about two metres between hives
- hives on stands. Hive stands should be high enough to place the top of the brood box level with your closed fist when standing with your arms at your side. This will reduce the risk of back pain through poor working posture when inspecting your bees. Hive stands will also aid the air flow underneath the hive. WBC hives come with integral, rather short legs.

It is sometimes difficult to meet all these conditions and your final choice of site may be a compromise on some of these desirable features.

The hedge will raise the bees' flight path above neighbours' heads. The National hive in the middle of the group of three is the first stage of a swarm control procedure and the one on the right of the picture is a WBC hive

4 EQUIPMENT

First of all, don't be tempted to rush out and buy anything until you have had a chance to find out what options are available. There are several choices to be made and it is worth while biding your time and talking to experienced beekeepers about the advantages and disadvantages of the various choices. You should obtain the catalogues of beekeeping equipment from the main suppliers. Some contain useful information about the use of the equipment. The main suppliers in the British Isles can be found on the internet.

If you intend buying a beginners' kit make sure you know exactly what it contains. Are the hive, floor, frames, queen excluder, smoker, bee suit, hive tool and beginners' book in the kit the type you would have chosen? Be wary of second-hand 'bargains'. There are some to be had but it pays to get help from an experienced beekeeper before you buy. Tread with care at second-hand beekeeping equipment auctions.

The following paragraphs are my comments on some of the equipment you will need. These are based on my experience with WBC hives many years ago and currently with National hives. Perhaps they will help you even if you decide to buy other types of hives and equipment after your discussions in your beginners' course and with beekeepers in your local group. A complete list of the equipment you need to start keeping bees in your first year is shown in Appendix 1.

Personal protection

It is important to have good protection from bee stings when you attend demonstrations. The face, especially the eyes, should always be well protected. The wrists and ankles are also more sensitive than other areas of the body. Good protection will give you confidence to concentrate on learning what is being demonstrated instead of worrying about stings.

The bee suit may be the first item you need to buy. I have found a single piece overall more convenient than separate trousers and jacket. A detachable hat-cum-veil which can be unzipped and thrown back is useful in warm weather. Also it can be washed by hand or in a bag such as a pillow case separately from the overall giving the veil a longer life.

I stopped using kid gloves during my first season with bees because they are too thick to handle frames and they become contaminated with dried venom. The dried venom can alert the guard bees and heavily propolised thick gloves are difficult to wash. Instead I suggest that you use washing-up gloves. They can be washed clean and make handling frames easier.

The ankles can be very sensitive to a bee sting and need protection. The bees can sting through thin woollen or cotton socks. So use boots and thick socks with your trousers tucked into the socks to prevent the bees walking up inside your trousers. For maximum security use wellingtons.

Hives

The hives and the moveable frames for the beeswax combs are made to precise dimensions to allow for a space for the bees to move around between the frames and the sides of the hive. This is known as 'bee space' and is between 6.5 and 9 mm. The bees will use a sticky substance, propolis collected from tree buds, to fill a gap less than 'bee space' and they will build wax 'brace comb' across a gap greater than 9 mm. Standard National and WBC hives have a bee space below the frames, called bottom bee space, and other types have a bee space above the frames, top bee space.

One important decision before you get your bees is which type of hive to choose. You may in time want to keep more colonies and it is important to stick to one type of hive because having different types can make it very inconvenient for swarm control, for example, and when adding supers.

The choice of hive is a much debated subject and the pros and cons of the different types are discussed in beekeeping books. For beginners one important consideration is which hive most beekeepers in your locality use, because at first you may need help with frames of bees or brood and it's much easier if you use the same frame size as your mentor or helper.

The National, sometimes more precisely referred to as the Modified National, is the most popular hive in the British Isles, the Smith is popular in Scotland and the north of England, and the Langstroth is the most popular worldwide. The traditional WBC hive is considered by many to be the prettiest hive and a few of these hives at the bottom of the garden can be very attractive. Applying the treatment to control and monitor the varroa mite is not as straightforward with a WBC as for the National hive. The frames for the WBC and the National are interchangeable. I started with WBC hives but after about three years I changed to Nationals.

So do discuss hive types with local beekeepers in your group before deciding which type to have.

Whichever type of hive you finally choose, make sure you buy an open mesh floor (OMF) for each one. As well as providing improved ventilation, the OMF enables you to monitor the varroa mite population easily. You need this information so that you can use appropriate treatment to control varroa and maintain a healthy colony. Another advantage of the OMF compared to the solid floor is that varroa mites that fall off the bees fall through the floor and are unable to climb back on to the bees. This helps to reduce the population of mites. If you decide to buy second-hand hives be sure to replace the traditional solid floor with an OMF.

National hive

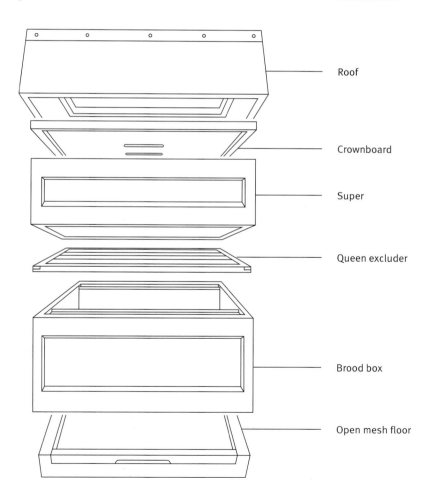

Roof

Crownboard

Super

Queen excluder

Brood box

Open mesh floor

Alex Ellis

Brood frames with foundation. Note the
position of the frame nails

Brood frames

There are several types of frames and the choice can be very
confusing. I soon discarded frames for the brood box with end
spacers in favour of Hoffman self-spacing frames. Many of the
frames listed in the suppliers' catalogues will result in spaces
between the adjacent frames being much greater than 'bee space'.
Such spaces attract the building of brace comb making removing
the frames during examinations more difficult.

The frames I use for National hives are made up from 27 mm
wide top bars, wide side bars (with Hoffman self-spacing wings
35 mm and the remainder of the bar 27 mm) and wide bottom bars.
These bottom bars comprise two pieces with shoulders and are also
described as bottom bars for Manley super frames. The assembled
frames are 27 mm wide (top, side and bottom) except where they
are in contact at the spacing wings. The remainder of the frames
have a gap of 8 mm between adjacent frame surfaces, a correct
bee space. This means less brace comb and therefore easier comb
removal. Also these frames are stronger than the slimmer types and
can be recycled and fitted with new foundation. They can last for
many years.

If you decide to use these frames in your brood chamber you
need to specify the parts carefully. The nearest frame listed in the
catalogues is a DN5 but these do not always include the wide top,
side and bottom bars. I suggest that you persevere when you are
ordering these brood frames.

Some beekeepers fit 12 frames in a National brood box. I prefer
to use 11 frames with a 'dummy board'. This is a solid wooden
board the same size as a frame to replace a frame or to fill a space
less than a frame would occupy. A dummy board is easier to
remove than the 12th frame, and leaves enough space to carry out
a complete examination without having to leave a frame outside the
brood box. At the end of the examination the dummy board makes
it easier to push up the combs close together by gently levering the
hive tool between the side of the hive and dummy board.

Super frames

Frames with end spacers are more flexible than Hoffman self
spacing frames for supers. Narrow (37 mm) spacers are used for
super frames with foundation but when the comb has been drawn
out the frames may be given wider spacing by using the wide
(50 mm) spacers or alternate wide and narrow spacers. This is done

so that a super can be filled with honey using eight or nine frames instead of 10 for a WBC hive or 11 for a National to save on frames and labour when extracting. This may be worth while for a beekeeper with many hives but is probably not a significant saving if you have only one or two hives. Plastic spacers are better than metal ends, which can easily cut your fingers when you are cleaning the frames. Supers fitted with castellated spacers are not so flexible as they have to be used with the same number of frames with drawn comb or foundation.

Making up frames

Ready-assembled frames complete with foundation are available from the equipment suppliers but most beekeepers buy frame parts and make up the frames themselves. I have found that making up the frames using a 'rampin' with moulding pins much easier than a hammer and frame nails. For fixing the side bars to the top bar I use 20 mm moulding pins and for fixing the bottom bars to the side bars and the wedge 15 mm moulding pins. Panel pins tend to split the wood.

Queen excluders

You will also need a queen excluder. The flat slotted metal type is satisfactory for a hive with bottom bee space such as the National and WBC because the flat excluder is supported by the top of the frames, which are flush with the top edge of the brood box.

Smoker, fuel, hive tools and cover cloths

The framed wire excluder is suitable for either top or bottom bee space hives. The bees appear to use more brace comb and propolis on the flat excluder so the framed wire excluder is easier to remove to carry out the weekly examination. Also the framed wire excluder is easier to clean because it has not attracted so much burr wax and propolis.

Other essentials are a hive tool and smoker. The larger smokers are easier to light and stay alight longer than small ones.

Reserve hive

You need a reserve hive for swarm control. It is likely that your bees will not swarm in their first year but it can happen. I recommend that you buy a reserve hive when you get your main hive as it is very difficult to manage a swarming colony without it. A reserve hive may be useful to hold a second swarm from an apiary other than your own. The spare floor and brood box will be useful when you come to 'spring clean' your main hive.

There are advantages in maintaining a minimum of two stocks. You may wish to set up the additional colony in your second year, initially bringing your reserve hive into permanent use. Now you will of course need aother reserve hive. So your reserve hive including the full complement of frames needs to be interchangeable with your other equipment.

New or used equipment

Will you buy new equipment or look for bargains at auctions or the 'For Sale' columns in *Bee Craft*? You can choose new hives already assembled or as flat packs for you to assemble at home. If you are put off buying new hives because of the cost, why not enquire about special winter offers from the equipment suppliers?

I suggest that you get help from an experienced beekeeper before you buy any second-hand equipment. Wood shrinks and you need to be sure that the various parts fit well together. Used WBC hive parts are particularly prone to shrinkage resulting in gaps between the boxes which allow wasps, and bees from other hives, to enter and steal honey. Second-hand hives sometimes do not have the correct bee space because of shrinkage. Sometimes this can be corrected but not always.

All second-hand woodwork should be scorched to reduce the risk of introducing disease to your new bees. Use a blowlamp to scorch the wood, paying particular attention to corners. Don't forget to remove plastic runners before you start. Do not buy any frames containing used comb. Any you acquire in a job lot should be burned straight away because beeswax can carry disease.

5 HEALTH MATTERS

The main purpose of good beekeeping practice is to keep your bees healthy. Here are some of the main points:

Healthy capped brood with a pollen arch and sealed honey

- a good site for your apiary and how the hives are arranged provides shelter from wind, frost pockets and damp areas
- a sound well maintained hive with an open mesh floor helps to create a well ventilated atmosphere in the hive during the summer and prevents damp in winter
- make sure that any bees you bring into your apiary are healthy. If you are starting with a swarm carry out a health check on the developing brood. Ask an experienced beekeeper to help if necessary
- clean and scorch with a blow lamp all second-hand wooden equipment before use, and do not use any second-hand comb. Clean and scorch brood boxes every spring to reduce the load of disease spores in the hive
- always use clean tools, overalls and gloves
- reduce the risk of starting a spate of robbing by keeping bits of wax and propolis and spare frames with food in a bee-proof container. Also avoid spilling honey or sugar syrup in the apiary. Robbing bees may bring disease spores back to their colony
- feed your bees with only sugar syrup, fondant or your own honey or frames of food from healthy colonies in your own apiary. Avoid the risk of bees clearing out the remnants from honey jars. Honey can carry the spores of AFB
- make sure that all the colonies involved in any frame transfers or other manipulations are healthy
- replace three or four of the darkest or most damaged combs, including those with patches of drone cells, every spring. This will reduce the load of spores of nosema and chalkbrood in the combs
- look out for any unusual larvae or cell cappings every time you carry out your regular examination, and make a specific disease examination of the brood combs every spring and autumn.

During your first year with bees I suggest that you learn to recognise healthy bees and brood. Very soon you will be able to see anything that appears unusual and get some advice straight away.

HEALTHY BEES

Healthy bees will be busy foraging in good weather, bringing in pollen and nectar, and you can see this simply by looking at the entrance. When you are examining the brood, check that the frames and comb are clean without any light brown marks.

You can compare the colony's development and level of activity with others in the apiary. If you have only one or two colonies keep in touch with other local beekeepers and compare progress with a number of colonies in a similar environment to your own.

Healthy brood

Healthy brood is in a compact oval shape, with brood of about the same age together, indicating that the queen lays the eggs in a regular circular pattern. So look for eggs, open cells containing larvae and capped cells together, with only a few cells not in the appropriate age group. You need not be too concerned about a few empty cells, say up to 5% of the brood area, ignoring those that are in a straight line along the wire in the foundation.

There should be only one egg in each cell. Young larvae in the open cells are moist, pearly white and lying in the form of a 'c' in the cell, with segments of the body visible. Healthy sealed cells have cappings that are regular, dry, biscuit-coloured and slightly domed. Drone cells are slightly larger than worker cells and have a more pronounced dome.

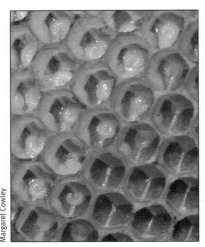

Margaret Cowley

Healthy eggs and larvae in cells means one egg in each cell and larvae that are glistening white with visible segments and lying in the form of a 'c'

Healthy brood showing capped worker cells and the larger domed drone cells along the top of the frame. The queen cell in the bottom left hand corner can easily be missed when it is covered with bees

You can compare what you see with the many excellent pictures of healthy and diseased brood in the publications produced to help beekeepers to identify disease. See Appendix 3 for currently available publications.

DISABLING CONDITIONS AND DISEASE

It is quite normal for plants and animals to suffer disease and disability sometimes and bees are no exception. One of the advantages for bees kept in hives is that the beekeeper can look out for any problems that crop up and deal with them. Some diseases are notifiable and it is the beekeeper's legal duty to report them to the appropriate authority. So you need to know the signs of a few of the main diseases that affect bees, and of course those that are notifiable.

You can get help to learn about disease from your local beekeepers' group as well as from experienced beekeepers. The governments of the UK and the Republic of Ireland provide advisory, training and education programmes for beekeepers as well as a bee health inspection and diagnostic service. Your local association or group is your best first contact and they can usually tell you about all the services available in your area and how to contact them.

Starvation

I understand that starvation is one of the main reasons for colony loss during the winter. There are other times when there may be a shortage of nectar or prolonged poor weather prevents the foragers going out. The first signs may be dead pupae being thrown out of the hive, or bees staggering about, and inside the hive piles of dead bees on the floor.

If you see these signs you should immediately spray sugar syrup on to the bees and pour some on to the bees between the frames. If you are not too late many of the bees will revive and be flying out quite soon. Now you can add a feeder with sugar syrup. Of course it is much better to avoid starvation by making sure your bees have food stores in the hive at all times.

Robbing

Bees are tempted to steal nectar or honey from another colony when supplies of nectar from flowers have suddenly dried up, such as after the spring and at the end of the main flow. Robbing can take place at any time and it will usually end with the loss of the robbed colony. Fortunately it is much easier to prevent robbing starting than to stop it.

You should keep small entrances and make sure that there are no little cracks or crannies the robbers can find. If the bees find some honey or sugar syrup spilled in the apiary the finder will take some home, give a taste to her sisters and do a round dance which tells them that there is a good source of food nearby. Out they go and search and perhaps find a poorly defended colony. So do avoid spills of honey, sugar syrup or bits of comb in the apiary.

Queenlessness

A small number of colonies become queenless during the winter due to the death of the queen when the colony is unable to replace her. During the active season queenlessness is usually caused by an error or accident by the beekeeper that leaves the colony 'hopelessly' queenless, that is without any means to replace the lost queen. After three days there will be no eggs and five days later no open cells with larvae, and after three weeks no brood at all. The colony will begin to dwindle and soon there will be laying workers.

During the active season you may find that there are no eggs while you are carrying out your regular examination. The presence of eggs is evidence enough that the queen was present during the last three days, but the absence of eggs does not necessarily mean the colony is queenless.

A queenless colony will probably be more irritable than usual with the bees wandering about aimlessly on the comb. There will be very few if any cells polished up ready for the queen to lay in and pollen in cells may appear shiny because it is covered with honey to prevent mould developing while it is not being used. However, none of these signs is conclusive evidence that there is no queen present in the colony.

To confirm whether or not your colony is queenless you need to introduce a test frame with brood including eggs taken from another healthy colony. If after four days you find that queen cells have been started you can be sure that the colony is queenless. You can leave one of the started queen cells to develop and after three or four weeks you should have a young mated queen in the hive.

If no queen cells are started there is a queen present that for some reason is not laying. Look carefully on the test frame, where you will usually find her. She may be a young queen that has not yet started laying or an old queen that has given up. A young queen will soon start laying and all will be well. If she is an old queen you should replace her with a young mated laying queen.

Drone-laying queen

The signs are patches of large domed drone capping on worker cells, gradually replacing all of the worker brood. The brood area is compact but 'untidy', and you may see stunted drones that emerge from worker cells. The queen is running out of her store of sperm and can lay only unfertilised eggs. This may be because of the queen's old age or perhaps poor weather during the previous summer resulting in poor mating. The solution is to remove the drone-laying queen and introduce a young queen or unite the bees to a queenright colony if you have one.

Domed cappings on worker cells in a group like this is a sign of a drone-laying queen or, if here and there all over the comb, of laying workers

Laying workers

The large domed drone cappings on worker cells are not in a compact group as for a drone-laying queen but are distributed haphazardly on the comb. You may find more than one egg in some cells and eggs attached to the side of the cell. This condition arises when the colony has had no queen for three weeks or more. It is not worth while uniting to another or attempting to introduce a new queen as she will be killed by the laying workers. The easiest way to deal with this colony is to shake the bees into some long grass, say about 50 metres from the apiary, and let those that can fly return and beg their way into another colony. The laying workers are unable to fly and will die. You should take away all parts of the hive and stand before depositing the bees in the long grass otherwise the bees will simply return to the empty hive or cluster on the hive stand.

Chilled brood

Patches of eggs, larvae and pupae die and turn black. This is caused by not enough bees being available to keep the brood warm or by brood being left exposed for too long in cold weather. It may occur when a colony has built up quickly in the warm early spring followed by a prolonged cold spell. Another likely cause is the beekeeper rearranging the brood nest by mistake or accident, placing empty comb or foundation in the middle of the brood nest.

Bald brood

This is usually caused by wax moth larvae that chew through cappings, covering the straight line of open cappings with a silky substance. This is removed by the bees leaving the pupae exposed but unharmed. Bald brood does not present a serious problem to strong colonies but beekeepers often follow the silky trail with the hive tool and kill the wax moth larva when it appears.

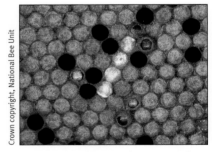

Crown copyright, National Bee Unit

Bald brood and wax moth activity. Follow the silky trail with your hive tool or tap the frame and the wax moth larva will often emerge

VARROA

Varroa destructor, a mite first seen in the UK in 1992, is an external parasite of honey bees. It has now spread throughout the British Isles. The mites feed on both brood and adult bees causing minor injury, weakening them and spreading harmful viruses. The population of mites can increase very quickly in untreated colonies and the colony will die. As yet we can not eradicate varroa but we can keep healthy productive colonies if we keep the mite population at a low level.

Keeping varroa mite populations at a low level throughout the year must be one of the aims of every beekeeper. I am therefore recommending that as soon as you have bees you start straight away to learn and practise varroa population control. There are a number of methods available for monitoring the varroa population in a colony, and a combination of treatments to control the level of mite population depending on the time of the year. These are often referred to as 'Integrated Pest Management' or 'IPM'. Detailed description of varroa and its monitoring and control is provided in *Managing Varroa* (see Appendix 3).

Monitoring varroa

Monitoring mite population is straightforward with an open mesh floor (OMF). You place the clean insert beneath the OMF and count the dead mites that fall on the insert over a period of seven or eight days to give you a reliable average daily mite drop. I have found it easier to count dead mites after only three or four days and repeat this after cleaning the insert and replacing it under the OMF. Leaving the insert in for the total of seven or eight days without a break sometimes results in a lot of accumulated debris on the insert, making it more difficult to see the mites.

If for any reason you are having difficulty seeing the mites because of the debris, scrape it into a container and mix with methylated spirit. The mites will float to the surface and most of the debris will sink to the bottom of the container. I have found that a glass or opaque plastic container and a torch or sunshine make it easier to see the mites.

You should remove the insert after the test so that the mites that fall off the bees will fall through to the ground and are unable to climb back into the colony. Some researchers have found that about 20% of varroa mites fall off their host within three days of emergence. So the OMF provides some control and helps to keep mite numbers down as well as providing a simple method for monitoring mite population.

You need to refer to *Managing Varroa* to use the daily mite drop number to decide on the level of control treatment needed to protect your bees from a potentially harmful level of varroa population. From March to July an average daily mite drop of two or fewer indicates a light infestation. Average daily mite drop above two means that some control needs to be applied. If the figure is above eight there is a high risk to the colony and effective control is needed promptly.

Drone brood removal

This is another tool we can use to monitor and control the varroa mite. It is simple and easy to use and does not introduce any chemicals into the colony. It exploits the mite's ·preference for raising its young on drone pupae rather than in worker brood. I suggest that you do this in your second year and beyond with bees because a nucleus or small colony are not likely to build drone cells.

You should replace one of the brood frames with a shallow frame with worker foundation. This frame should be placed two or three frames from the hive wall. The bees usually build natural drone comb underneath the shallow and before the drone cells are sealed, the female mites enter the cell to raise four or five offspring. When the drone comb is full of sealed drone cells and varroa you can cut it off the frame and destroy it. You must of course do this before the drones emerge, otherwise you are helping to raise more varroa mites.

If you are not monitoring the varroa using the OMF you can get an idea of the infestation level by examining a sample of drone pupae before you cut it all off the frame. You may need practice and some help at first. You slide the prongs of an uncapping fork beneath the darker coloured cappings of the older pupae and lift it

Varroa mites prefer to reproduce on drone pupae so drone brood removal can help to control the varroa population

Crown copyright, National Bee Unit

out. The mites can be seen on the white drone pupae quite easily and the infestation level estimated from the proportion of pupae with mites by referring to *Managing Varroa*.

I prefer to monitor using the OMF but I always have one shallow frame in each of my brood chambers. This provides additional means to control varroa if needed and encourages the bees to concentrate drone cell building in one place instead of on a number of brood frames.

Pyrethroid resistance

Most beekeepers in this country now have varroa mites that are resistant to pyrethroid treatments such as Apistan and Bayvarol. You can find out if the mites in your hive are resistant to these pyrethroids by asking experienced beekeepers in your local group or your neighbouring beekeepers. If they have resistant mites you almost certainly do as well.

If you are not sure, I suggest that you use Apiguard, which is effective for all mites. Apiguard needs to be in the hive for six weeks and is most effective when the outside temperature is above 15°C. Apilife Var, an alternative to Apiguard, is now authorised for use against varroa in the UK. The main active ingredient as for Apiguard is thymol and the product is supported by many years' experience in Europe. No doubt more treatments will be registered in due course and will be welcomed by beekeepers.

Full details of the biology and harmful effects of the varroa mite on honeybee colonies as well as methods of monitoring and control are provided in *Managing Varroa*. A description of the methods of monitoring and treatment that I have used and found to be simple and effective is included in the months when the procedure is applied. However I suggest that you discuss monitoring and control methods with experienced beekeepers and bee inspectors in your area and find out what is best for your situation.

Chalkbrood

Chalkbrood is a very common disease caused by a fungus called *Ascosphaera apis*. The cells are uncapped by the bees and dead larvae appear as hard chalky white or mottled grey remains called mummies that often take up the hexagonal form of the cell. You may see mummies on the hive floor and outside the entrance. Signs of chalkbrood can be seen in most colonies at some time, though

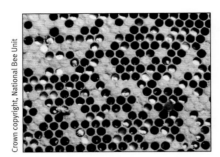

Crown copyright, National Bee Unit

Chalk brood can be seen in most colonies in the early spring and it usually disappears as the colony develops and the weather improves. This is a serious outbreak

it is not often serious. It is more likely to affect weak colonies in the early spring, usually clearing up as the weather improves and the colony develops. It can be controlled by maintaining strong colonies and changing the queen in persistent cases.

Nosema

This widespread disease is caused by a single celled organism called *Nosema apis* and recently also by another species, *Nosema ceranae*. The spores multiply in the adult bee's gut and are eventually passed out in the faeces.

The effect of Nosema on the colony may be insignificant if only a few individual bees are infected. You cannot see any signs of the disease on individual bees. Seriously affected colonies often suffer from dysentery and the first signs you may see in the spring are light brown marks around the entrance of the hive and on the combs. This does not necessarily mean that the colony is suffering from Nosema. It is spread through the colony by young bees cleaning soiled combs and becoming infected. Badly infected colonies fail to build up in the spring and will produce little or no surplus honey. Nosema and some other not so common adult bee diseases can be confirmed only by taking a sample of about 30 bees for microscopic analysis.

Lightly infected colonies will probably recover quite quickly as the weather improves. The recommended treatment for badly infected colonies is to move the colony on to sterilised drawn comb or clean foundation. If you suspect that your colony is badly infected ask for advice from an experienced beekeeper.

Acarine

Serious incidence of this disease is now fairly rare with our native bees in the UK. There are few visible signs indicating the presence of acarine but badly infected bees are unable to fly, and they crawl up grass stems around the hive entrance, with their wings set at unusual angles. The cause is a parasitic mite *Acarapis woodi* which lives in the bees' breathing tubes, the trachea, in the thorax. The disease can be confirmed by dissecting the bees under a microscope and examining the trachea for mites. There is no recommended treatment for acarine.

Sacbrood

This is a virus disease usually affecting only a few larvae in a diseased colony. It does not usually cause any serious problem but the signs can be mistaken for American foulbrood (AFB). Look out for larvae that have become fluid-filled sacs in cells that have been uncapped. The dried larva darkens in colour and the resulting scale can be easily removed using a matchstick. This is a useful check to confirm that it is not the notifiable disease known as AFB. There is no recommended treatment for sacbrood.

Sac brood. A fluid filled larval skin that may be removed by a matchstick confirms that it is sac brood

Crown copyright, National Bee Unit

European foulbrood (EFB)

This is caused by a bacterium called *Melissococcus plutonius*. The larvae in unsealed cells are misshapen and lying in an unnatural attitude in the cell. The larvae may appear 'melted down' and turn pale yellow in colour. Ask for advice even if you see only one or two affected larvae. As more larvae are affected the brood pattern will become patchy. There may be an unpleasant odour.

EFB can be seen in open cells with discoloured and misshapen larvae

Crown copyright, National Bee Unit

American foulbrood (AFB)

This is caused by a bacterium called *Paenibacillus larvae*. The affected larvae die in sealed cells causing the appearance of the cappings to change. You can see that some of the cells have

AFB. The cell cappings may appear sunken and damp with perforations. The ropiness test is confirmation

sunken cappings with small irregular perforations. Some may appear damp or greasy and darker in colour than other cells. By inserting a matchstick in the cell you can withdraw the contents slowly as a dark brown mucus-like 'rope' 10 to 30 mm long. Ask for advice as soon as you see one or two cells.

EFB and AFB are notifiable diseases

Both EFB and AFB are notifiable diseases and if you suspect their presence you are legally required to notify the appropriate authorities as soon as possible. In England and Wales you should contact your local Seasonal or Regional Bee Inspector, or the National Bee Unit (NBU) direct. You should also close up the hive and reduce the entrance to prevent robbing. Sterilise beekeeping equipment before opening any other colonies. You must not remove any hives, equipment, bees or honey from the apiary until you are cleared to do so by the bee inspector, who will arrange an inspection visit as soon as possible.

Future threats

Future threats to our honey bees include the **Small Hive Beetle (SHB)**, **Tropilaelaps** and the **Asian hornet**. These have not been seen in the British Isles as yet (2010). Tropilaelaps is similar to varroa in many ways. The Asian hornet is active throughout France. You should report to the appropriate authorities if you suspect that SHB or Tropilaelaps is in your hive. See Appendix 3 for publications showing full details of these threats. You can keep yourself informed about how these threats develop by maintaining contact with local groups of beekeepers, from *Bee Craft*, *BBKA News* and *Beekeeper's Quarterly* journal, and by registering on Beebase.

6 SWARMING

DELAYING SWARMING

Swarming is a natural process that enables the bees to reproduce colonies and at the same time replace an ageing queen with a young one. I do not expect we will ever be able to prevent but we can delay swarming. A healthy thriving colony may be inclined to swarm once in a season. Others may swarm in their second or even third season. We usually get five days' notice that the colony is likely to swarm, when we see larvae with food in developing queen cells.

Queen cell production is mainly triggered by the diminishing queen substance reaching each worker. The queen's genes and age play a part. Some colonies are more inclined to swarm than others and the quantity of queen substance a queen produces declines after she reaches 18 months of age. Other factors include the availability of early crops such as oilseed rape, good weather and congestion in the colony that interferes with the distribution of queen substance.

When you start with your first colony you will not be able to do much about most of the factors that trigger swarming but you can prevent congestion. This is why you should regularly check if the colony has room to expand. Early in the season make sure that there is space in the brood nest for the queen to lay eggs and that there is plenty of space in the supers for storing nectar and for bees to park at night and during poor weather.

A prime swarm which can be shaken into a box or swarm-catching bag on a pole

Margaret Cowley

Queen cells. The central cell is open. The two outer ones are sealed. The colony has probably swarmed

A small swarm settled in an ideal position for shaking into a skep or box. It may be a secondary swarm or cast

Another way to reduce congestion is by taking out some frames with bees and brood to make a nucleus and replace them with clean drawn comb. When you learn to raise your own queens you will be able to keep young queens and avoid rearing queens from eggs produced by queens that show a high inclination to swarm. I would encourage you to learn these procedures as soon as you have mastered the basics. They are described in Chapter 20.

SWARM CONTROL

As soon as you find queen cells with larvae and food you should adopt your chosen method to manage the swarming procedure so that you don't lose half of your bees and probably your entire honey crop for the year.

There are many different procedures you can use. If you have started using a particular method you have learned from an experienced beekeeper, persevere with it so that you become confident with one method before you try another. Don't try to follow bits of different methods. Once you have mastered one procedure and understand the principles then you can experiment if you wish. You can think of the colony made up of three parts, the queen, the brood and 'house' bees, and the flying bees or foragers. Most if not all swarm control methods involve separating one of these parts from the other two.

The artificial swarm

Probably the most widely used method is known as the artificial swarm. The basic method was described by J W Pagden in the 1870s and is included in many books about beekeeping. This method will maintain the maximum foraging force with the queen. She resumes egg-laying with only a short interruption which therefore minimises the loss of honey. If you follow the procedure carefully and do not miss seeing any queen cells it nearly always works.

You will need your reserve hive comprising brood box, floor, crownboard, roof and a full complement of frames with foundation. A few frames with drawn comb will be useful but most beginners in their first two or three seasons are unlikely to have spare drawn comb. The following method is based on the traditional artificial swarm, slightly modified to work with mostly foundation.

As soon as you see open, that is unsealed, queen cells and there are no sealed queen cells, you should create an artificial swarm straight away. Do not destroy any queen cells and do not shake any bees off the combs at this stage because this is likely to injure the developing queen. Instead gently push the bees aside with your finger so you can see the whole of the comb and especially around the edges where you often find partly hidden queen cells.

You may gently brush the bees off the comb if you want to remove all the bees, again taking care of all the queen cells. You can complete your initial examination of each comb and note how many open queen cells there are and on which frames.

You will have already taken off the roof, supers and queen excluder. Now proceed as follows:

The artificial swarm

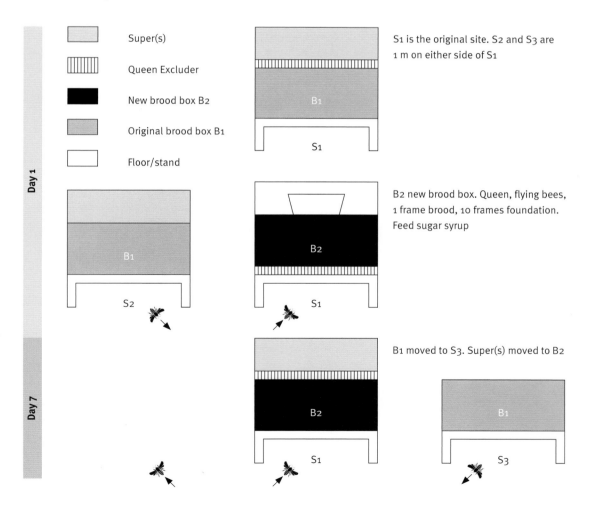

S1 is the original site. S2 and S3 are 1 m on either side of S1

B2 new brood box. Queen, flying bees, 1 frame brood, 10 frames foundation. Feed sugar syrup

B1 moved to S3. Super(s) moved to B2

Super(s)

Queen Excluder

New brood box B2

Original brood box B1

Floor/stand

Day 1

Day 7

1. Move the brood box B1 and floor with brood, bees and queen, to hive stand S2 about 1 metre to the side with the entrance facing the same direction.
2. Place the floor on the original site S1, then the queen excluder, and on top of the queen excluder the spare brood box B2, with frames of foundation. Remove one frame of foundation from the centre of B2 and keep it for later. *(The queen excluder is placed underneath the brood box to prevent the flying bees and queen absconding or a swarm leaving if new queen cells are built on older larvae. As there is a space underneath, a framed queen excluder should be used.)*
3. Examine the colony in B1, select a frame with the queen, and a small area of brood in all stages, but no queen cells, and place it in the middle of B2 on S1. Place any available drawn comb on both sides of the introduced frame so that there is room for the queen to resume laying straight away.
4. Close up the frames in B1 and add the spare frame of foundation removed from B2. Add any supers on to B1 then the crownboard and roof. If there are no supers, feed sugar syrup two days later. If you feed straight away there is a risk of starting robbing. *(All the flying bees from B1 will return to the original site S1 and enter brood box B2. There is no need for you to reduce the number of queen cells in B1 because the house bees, feeling less crowded, will do this for you, leaving one daughter queen cell.)*
5. Feed sugar syrup to the bees in brood box B2 on site S1 until the foundation is drawn out. *(You have now created an artificial swarm comprising the old queen and mainly flying bees in B2 on the original site S1.)*

After seven days:

6. Move the original brood box B1 to S3 about 1 metre on the opposite side of S1. *(Because you left only open queen cells, the first virgin queen will not emerge for at least eight days, that is after the move to S3. The bees that have become flyers during the week will now return to S2 and finding there is no hive will return to the nearest hive on the original site S1, reinforcing the foraging force in B2. This will also reduce the risk of a cast (a secondary swarm with a virgin queen) leaving after the queen emerges because there are now few if any flyers in B1.)*
7. Examine B2 to check that the old queen has resumed laying and remove any new queen cells. Remove the queen excluder when the queen has resumed laying. Stop feeding sugar syrup when the foundation in the brood box is

fully drawn out and transfer the supers from B1 to B2 above a queen excluder. Check that B1 has food in the brood box when moving the supers back to B2 and feed B1 if needed.

After another 14 to 21 days:
8. Check that the new queen has started to lay in B1.
9. You can unite the new colony in B1 to the one in B2 on the original site S1, first of all removing the old queen, any time up to September.

You have controlled swarming and replaced the old queen with a young queen. If you wish to increase the number of colonies you can prepare both colonies for the winter but the old queen will almost certainly swarm again next season.

If you can't find the queen:

It can sometimes be difficult to find a queen when the bees are thinking of swarming because there are so many bees in the hive. It can be very useful to have marked queens in your hives. If you have been unable to find the queen by examining each comb you can still control swarming by creating an artificial swarm.

1. As you examine the combs (stage 3 above) in B1 select a comb with some brood in all stages but no queen cells, and place it in the new brood box B2 on the original site S1.
2. Now carefully brush all the bees off all the combs in B1 into the spare box B2 on the original site taking care to avoid damaging the queen cells, replacing all the combs, some with brood and queen cells but no bees, into the original brood box B1.
3. When you are sure that all the bees are in the spare box on the original site replace its queen excluder and supers, then lift B1, the brood box with combs, open queen cells and no bees, on top of the supers. Replace the crownboard and roof and leave it for two or three hours or overnight. (*This will allow time for the nurse bees to move up to cover the brood and keep it warm, leaving the queen and mainly flying bees in the bottom box.*)
4. Lift the brood box B1 containing combs of brood and nurse bees on to the floor about 1 metre to one side of the original site. You can now replace the crownboard and roof on both hives and proceed from Item 2 above.

A sealed queen cell with a thinned tip indicating that the queen will soon emerge

The queen has emerged. There may be remnants of food in the cell

The queen has emerged leaving the lid still attached. Sometimes a worker bee is trapped inside with the lid closed

Margaret Cowley

If you find open and sealed queen cells:

Sometimes even experienced beekeepers can miss seeing an open queen cell and find sealed queen cells at the next inspection. If this is the case then you either missed an examination or if you were careful in following the seven-day plan, you missed seeing queen cells during the last visit. It is easy to miss occupied queen cells tucked into the edge of the comb along the side or bottom of the frame.

The swarm probably left the hive on the day or day after the first queen cell was sealed. The bees sometimes delay their departure because of bad weather. Has a swarm already left? Has a virgin queen emerged? You need to know the answers before you decide how to prevent the loss of more bees in a secondary swarm or cast.

An experienced beekeeper may be able to decide what to do but if you are a beginner you may find it helpful to follow the decision chart shown opposite.

First look for eggs or young larvae. Also look for tiny larvae that are just beginning to form an open 'c'. Larvae that make a well formed 'c' are more than two days old.

If there are no eggs or young larvae it's very likely that the swarm has already flown off with the old queen. Select the best open queen cell and mark the frame with a drawing pin in the top bar above the cell. The selected cell should be surrounded by worker brood and contain a well developed pearly white larva in an ample bed of royal jelly. Handle the frame with the selected cell with care, brushing bees off rather than shaking it.

Next find out if a virgin queen has emerged. You will need to check all the sealed queen cells by gently touching the tip with your hive tool to see if the hinged cap has been closed after the queen emerged. The workers do this quite often, sometimes closing a worker bee scavenging the remains of the royal jelly inside.

If you find that a cell is empty, a virgin queen has probably emerged; she may be in the hive or she could have left with a secondary swarm or cast. In this case, it is likely that there are other sealed cells with virgins ready to emerge, so you can open all the sealed queen cells with the tip of your hive tool, releasing all the virgin queens into the colony.

Next you must remove all the queen cells, including the cell you marked earlier. If you miss a queen cell you will still run the risk of another cast.

You may now have more than one virgin queen in the colony and they will sort themselves out leaving only one. A colony with more than one virgin queen will not swarm but miss one queen cell and a swarm or cast will probably result. A swarm that gets away is one beekeeper's misfortune and may be another beekeeper's opportunity.

Decision-making tree if you find open and sealed queen cells

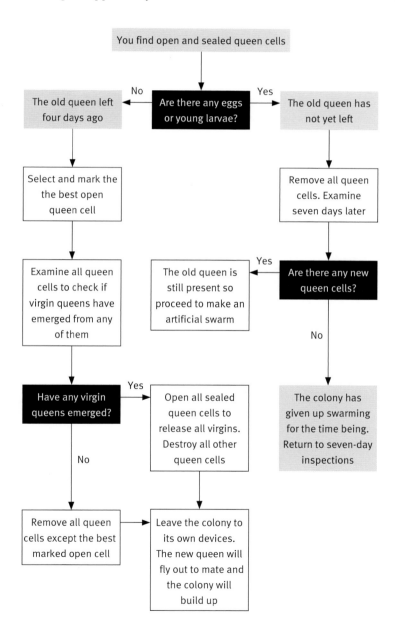

You find open and sealed queen cells

No ← Are there any eggs or young larvae? → Yes

The old queen left four days ago

The old queen has not yet left

Select and mark the the best open queen cell

Remove all queen cells. Examine seven days later

Examine all queen cells to check if virgin queens have emerged from any of them

Yes — The old queen is still present so proceed to make an artificial swarm

Are there any new queen cells?

No

Have any virgin queens emerged?

Yes → Open all sealed queen cells to release all virgins. Destroy all other queen cells

The colony has given up swarming for the time being. Return to seven-day inspections

No

Remove all queen cells except the best marked open cell → Leave the colony to its own devices. The new queen will fly out to mate and the colony will build up

RESCUING A SWARM

'A swarm in May is worth a load of hay' because it has time to settle and develop into a productive colony during the summer. In a good summer it can reward the rescuing beekeeper with a brood chamber and super full of drawn comb and a honey crop around the end of July. Collecting and hiving a swarm can also be fun and provides a useful service for your local community.

More often than not you do not know the origin of a swarm. There is a risk that it may be carrying disease, it may come from a 'swarmy' strain or be of poor temperament. I have been fortunate over many years and apart from some varroa infestation I have not yet collected a diseased swarm. Usually it is strong healthy colonies that swarm.

You will need a skep or strong cardboard box about the same size as a skep and a sheet of smooth porous material such as cotton, large enough to wrap around the box. Use glue or tape to fix the flaps forming the top of the box to the inside to create a smooth interior. This will prevent bees entering crevices beneath the flaps and being crushed when the box is moved.

When you are off to collect the swarm you should, of course, also take your veil and smoker. Some other useful aids include secateurs and a long pole with a swarm-catching bag to reach swarms just out of reach from the ground.

Swarms alight in all sorts of places. Do welcome the invitations to collect swarms that are easily accessible, for example on a light branch up to a couple of metres above the ground. Leave those

Here are some useful tools for rescuing swarms. On the table from the left, a skep or the alternative cardboard box, a swarm-catching bag and shallow box to carry the skep or box with the swarm wrapped in the sheet. With the three rods and the swarm catching bag you can reach a swarm up to 5 metres from the ground

that are high up in a tree or building to more experienced swarm collectors. Always avoid taking silly risks yourself. Be safety-conscious at all times towards helpers, onlookers and passers-by. Resist the temptation to climb a ladder to reach the one that is just out of reach from the ground.

Always remember to explain to the owner of the garden or land what you are going to do especially if you can see you will need to walk on to a flower bed or shake or cut off a small branch. It's also a good idea to say before you start that you will collect the swarm in the box in the evening. Try to attend to the swarm as soon as you see it or hear about one from a neighbour or swarm coordinator. Swarms seldom stay long in their first location.

Capturing the swarm

First of all spread the cotton sheet on the ground as near as you can to the swarm. Use some stones on the corners to prevent it being moved in the breeze. Now transfer the swarm cluster into the box. If the swarm is hanging from a branch, hold the box under the cluster and give the branch a sharp shake to dislodge the bees into the box. Sometimes the swarm is on a thin branch and it can be cut off and the swarm carefully deposited in the box. Clustering bees will usually walk up into a dark space so if they are on a post or where you can position the box above the swarm, you can wait until they have entered the dark space inside the box.

When you have most of the cluster in the box, place it upside down on the sheet and prop up one edge with a stone to create an entrance. By now there may be a lot of bees flying around and some will start to form another cluster on the branch. You can collect these in the same way with another small box and deposit them on to the sheet by the entrance. You may use the smoker to move them and give the site a good smoking to mask the smell of wax and bees remaining on the branch.

If you have the queen in the box you will see an increasing number of worker bees facing the entrance and raising their abdomens to expose their Nasonov glands and fanning. They are creating a flow of air to send the 'come and join us' pheromone into the surrounding area to guide the airborne bees to their new location. This is a good sign that the queen is present in your box. If the queen is not in the box there will be little or no fanning and the bees will soon abscond.

There may still be bees returning from foraging trips during the rest of the day so the best time to collect the boxed swarm is after

The swarm is shaken or brushed into the box and placed on the sheet with access for the bees. You can see many bees exposing their Nasonov gland and fanning to attract their sisters to the new location

The bees make their way into their new home. With patience you can sometimes catch sight of the queen

After about an hour nearly all the bees are in the hive

all have returned and stopped flying for the day. If you take them home during the day the returning bees will form another smaller cluster on the original site. Your neighbour will not be impressed, may be worried and will call you again. This time, without a queen it is not a swarm, and it will be impossible to collect the bees.

Collecting and hiving the swarm

Before you go to collect the swarm in the evening, prepare a hive with a full complement of frames and foundation. When you return to collect the swarm you will usually be greeted by a peaceful scene, no bees to be seen and all tucked up inside your box. Carefully fold and secure the sheet over the box and take it to your prepared hive. It is a good idea to 'hive' the swarm as soon as you can because there is a risk of suffocation if the swarm is left in the box overnight.

Sometimes but not often the box will be empty! The bees, even with a queen, have moved on. Have a look around but they are more likely to have moved by up to a mile or two. Better luck next time!

To hive the swarm, prop up a board against the hive entrance and cover it with the sheet then shake the bees out of the box on to it. Soon the bees will begin walking into the hive and if you watch you may see the queen. It may take up to an hour for all the bees to enter the hive.

Another quicker way is to dislodge the bees from the box straight into the hive after taking out the frames and temporarily closing the entrance. When you replace the frames, don't press them down on top of the bees. Let the frames sink slowly under their own weight.

Sometimes the bees abscond a day or two after you have placed them in a new home. Have a look around; they may have settled again nearby where you can collect them again. This time shake the swarm into a hive with a queen excluder underneath the brood box. The queen excluder should be removed after the swarm has started drawing out the foundation within three or four days.

Let the swarm use up the food the bees have brought with them in their crops to start drawing out the foundation for a couple of days. This is a precaution against disease that can be carried in the honey. Then you can feed with sugar syrup to help the swarm draw out the foundation. Examine the bees weekly and when available check that the open and sealed brood is healthy.

7 AUGUST

In August beekeepers start preparing for the new season. If we have made some mistakes then we can find out what went wrong by discussing them with experienced beekeepers. This way we can learn and improve our beekeeping for the coming year.

COLONY ACTIVITY

There will be a sharp decline in egg-laying as the main flow of nectar comes to an abrupt end towards the end of July or early August. Old queens may go off lay temporarily, resulting in little brood and no eggs or young larvae to be seen later on in the month. This does not necessarily mean that there is no queen in the hive. As soon as the nectar from the early autumn flowers is brought in by the foragers the queen resumes egg production.

There is a rapid fall in the adult population as the older foragers die after their hard work. The younger bees finish off ripening stores of nectar. Foragers continue to search for nectar and pollen.

Drones may be seen cowering in the corners of the hive and may be hassled by the workers. Soon the drones will be evicted and left to die outside.

Supersedure

If you started earlier in the year with a swarm or if you have a two-year-old queen in the colony the bees may have replaced the old queen with a new young queen without swarming. This is known as supersedure. You may find the old queen and her daughter, a new young queen, happily sharing the same comb. Beekeepers do not see this often, perhaps because the bees have superseded the queen quietly and without any fuss. You should leave well alone. If you introduced a new young queen bought in she would be killed.

Winter bees

The worker bees produced from August and into the autumn eat a lot of pollen, have a lot less brood to feed than the summer bees and also do less foraging. So they are able to build up stores of protein reserves known as fat bodies. Their lives are extended compared to the harder-worked summer bees. The worker bees in summer live for about six weeks while the winter workers live for about six months.

HELPING THE COLONY

You need to take off the honey as soon as it is ready at the end of July or early in August. This will give you enough time to apply the autumn treatment for varroa and start preparing the colony for winter.

Preparing for winter

These are the requirements for a colony to survive the winter:

- a sound hive
- a healthy colony
- a young queen
- a strong colony with plenty of young bees
- food stores to last from October to April
- protection from pests and predators.

This month you can make a start preparing for winter by dealing with the first four items on the list. Topping up the food stores and protecting the colony from pests and predators can be dealt with later.

A sound hive

Throughout the year bees need a sound waterproof hive, dry inside, with no leaks or small gaps in the joints. Robber bees can find the tiniest gaps at any time and wasps can be a nuisance in August.

The hives should be on hive stands to provide good all-round air circulation. Incidentally, to protect your back, the stands should be high enough so that the top of the brood box is level with your closed fist, when you are standing with your arms at your side.

Protection from extreme weather will be tested during the winter. Good air drainage, no frost pockets and shelter from prevailing winds are some other aspects to check. If there are any shortcomings with the condition of your hives, hive stands or their site, now is the time to make a start to improve the situation.

Some beekeepers winter their bees on a single brood chamber, others on a brood chamber and a super. I have found that a single National brood chamber works well for most of my colonies. I sometimes use a brood chamber and a super for large colonies. My bees winter well on either of these systems.

Some extra care is needed with a single National or WBC brood chamber. When you take off the supers with honey make sure that there is food in the brood box. If there was unused space in the supers as the flow came to an end it is likely that there is little or no food stored in the brood box. You should feed straight away if necessary. Also, in the early spring you may have to remove some brood frames still full of stores to make room as the queen increases her egg-laying.

A healthy colony

Throughout the active season, from April to July, you will have carried out a weekly examination during which you checked that the brood was healthy. No doubt you dealt with any health problems as soon as you noticed anything unusual in the brood combs.

A thorough health examination of the brood combs after shaking most of the bees off each comb is worth while before you plan your preparations for wintering. Examine any cells with an unusual appearance and try to find out the reason by looking at the signs. If you are at all concerned about the condition of even one cell ask for advice from your local bee inspector or an experienced beekeeper.

Young queens

A queen that has headed the colony for more than two seasons is more likely to die during the winter or become a drone-layer than a younger one. Young queens continue to lay longer into the autumn and start earlier in the spring than older queens.

If your colony swarmed during the season you will have a young queen in the colony. If you successfully managed swarming you have a young queen in one small colony and an older queen in the original colony. Now is the time to unite the colonies after removing the older queen. If you are not successful in finding the queen, you may have to resort to simply uniting the colonies and letting the queens sort themselves out. The younger queen usually wins. Of course, there is a risk of injury. Finding the queen is the better way.

If you want to keep both colonies, you can introduce a new young queen, if available, to replace a two-year-old queen. Queen introduction directly into a colony should not be attempted until the last few days of August or early September.

A strong colony with plenty of bees

A strong colony with plenty of young bees has a better chance of surviving the winter than a small colony. The population of bees falls quite rapidly after the main honey flow has stopped. The older bees who have worked so hard foraging come to the end of their lives.

A feed of sugar syrup after you have removed the honey crop will stimulate the queen to carry on egg-laying and this helps to increase the population of young bees. These are known as winter bees and are especially suited to survive the winter months.

If you collected some swarms in June or July they may not have had time to build up sufficiently to survive the winter. A small colony is best united to another larger colony to make a single more populous colony. Before you unite them, check that there is no disease in either of them.

Keeping varroa under control

One of the biggest risks to colony survival during the winter is a large number of varroa mites in the hive at the start of the winter. Autumn treatment is nearly always needed to ensure that there is the absolute minimum of mites in the colony at this time. If you did not monitor for varroa population in July you should do it early in August so that you can plan the appropriate treatment.

The treatment I use in the autumn is Apiguard, which is most effective when the outside temperature is above 15°C and needs to be in the hive for about six weeks. This means starting the treatment in mid August so that it is completed by the end of September. Afterwards it is a good idea to monitor the varroa population again to confirm that the treatment worked.

An eke is needed to extend the bee space above the brood frames to accommodate the Apiguard tray. The eke is a simple extension placed on the brood box to lift the crownboard. An empty super may be used as an eke. Do not forget to install the monitoring insert in the OMF to prevent the thymol fumes from escaping.

Beekeepers who take bees to the heather will start their winter preparations later. If you are planning to join the heather-going beekeepers, ask for their advice on the autumn treatment against varroa and other aspects of preparing the colony for winter.

Wasps

Wasps suffer from poor public relations but they provide a useful service to gardeners. They do eat many common garden pests in spring. In August they can be a real nuisance in the apiary as well as around the picnic area. They can overcome a colony once they have managed to get inside the hive. When this happens the bees seem to give up defending the entrance.

You can set up wasp traps around the outside of the apiary. If you site them too near the beehives they will attract the wasps to come in close to the hives. You can make your own traps by punching a hole in the lid of jars half filled with water or beer and some jam or fruit juice. Do not use honey because you do not want to trap and drown your bees.

I keep my colonies on small entrances of 80 to 100 mm and not more than 6 to 8 mm deep all the year round. A strong colony can easily defend this size of entrance against wasp invasion. The entrances on my nucleus hives are even smaller, 15 to 20 mm. Small entrances also help when the colony is defending itself against robber bees.

Robbing

Robbing can take place at any time but August and September present the biggest risk. You should keep small entrances as for preventing access by wasps and make sure that there are no little cracks the robbers could find. Also avoid spills of honey or sugar syrup in the apiary. When you remove the supers of honey always have them covered all the time as you move them from the hive to the bee-proof extracting room and of course as you return the wet supers to the hive. Keep the hive covered as much as you can when you are opening the hive to carry out beekeeping tasks.

Storing the supers

Supers full of drawn comb are a valuable asset and should be stored carefully ready for next spring. Stored comb is vulnerable to wax moth especially during the autumn. Wax moth prefers comb which has been used for raising brood but combs in supers are at risk too. Wax moth is active in warm weather so be sure not to delay preparing your super combs for winter storage.

I use 80% acetic acid to protect super combs from wax moth before storing them over winter. This treatment kills all stages of wax moth. The 80% strength acetic acid is available from the equipment suppliers. You should wear protective gloves and goggles when handling this strength acetic acid, and it is highly corrosive to metal and will damage concrete.

The supers and frames should be scraped clean of propolis and bits of brace and burr wax and you should remove any metal frame spacers. It's a good idea to smear any metal runners with petroleum jelly. Do not place the stack directly on to a concrete floor. The supers can be stacked on a wooden board such as a crownboard with the feed holes closed up. Place an absorbent pad in a shallow plastic tray on top of the frames in the top super in a stack of up to three boxes. Pour about 30 ml per super of acetic acid on to the pad. Place a wooden board on top of the stack and seal up the joints with tape or enclose it in a plastic bag such as a large 'wheely' bin bag. Leave it alone for at least a week for the heavy fumes to sterilise the combs.

Another method is to place the combs into a deep freeze for at least 24 hours. This kills all stages of wax moth. Alternatively you can buy Certan from the equipment suppliers. This biological larvicide is mixed with water and sprayed on the combs. This too kills all stages of wax moth, will not harm you or your bees and will not leave any trace in the wax or honey.

During mild autumn weather it would be a good idea to check that adult wax moth has not re-entered the supers. When the temperature is below 15°C the wax moth is not active and the supers with clean fumigated combs should be stacked on a mesh screen such as a queen excluder on a hive stand. Place another screen on top of the stack. The stack may be kept in a shed or outside under cover, or if not under cover add a roof on top which will allow air to circulate. This will prevent the combs becoming mouldy and mice will be kept out. A spider in the stack will be useful further protection against adult wax moth.

Until recently it was common practice for beekeepers in this country, Europe and America to use paradichlorbenzene (PDB) to protect comb from wax moth. There may be some still stored in beekeepers' sheds throughout the country. The use of this chemical is now illegal because it is carcinogenic and it leaves residues in the wax comb that can be transferred to the honey.

QUEEN INTRODUCTION

You must first of all remove the old queen and be sure that there is no queen in the colony. The young queen is placed in a queen introduction cage enabling the workers to feed and touch her with their antennae but prevent them attacking her. The cage is closed with a piece of newspaper and placed in the hive between two frames near any available brood. By the time the workers have chewed through the newspaper and released her they have had time to accept her as their own queen.

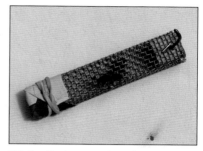

This is a Butler queen introduction cage. The bees can feed the queen through the cage. The paper cover on the end provides a refuge for the queen

If the introduction fails it will be impossible for the bees to produce their own queen because there will be no eggs, young larvae or drones available. If this is your first season with bees it may be advisable to ask for help from an experienced beekeeper, or perhaps the beekeeper who raised the new queen.

Queen introduction directly into a strong colony from May to mid August is unlikely to be successful and the new queen will probably be killed. Instead the new queen is introduced into a nucleus made up from the colony to be re-queened. Then the nucleus with the new laying queen is united to the queenless colony after a week or so.

UNITING

The first stage may take a few days because you need to bring the two colonies close together, to within about one metre. You should move a colony not more than about one metre every one or two good flying days. This gives the bees time to orientate to the hive's new location. During the day when you are ready to join the two colonies, you should make one queenless by removing the queen you do not wish to keep. Also, if necessary, clean off the brace comb from the top and bottom of the frames in both colonies. You can prepare the queen-right colony by placing a sheet of newspaper on top of the frames of the brood chamber and a queen excluder on top of the newspaper. Replace the crownboard and roof and leave until the evening.

The colonies to be united are gradually brought close together. A single sheet of newspaper is kept in place by a queen excluder

The colonies are assembled, initially separated by the newspaper, and left alone for five days

The bees nibble away at the paper and gradually mingle with the other colony

The rosebay willow herb is one of the best wild plants for bees throughout the British Isles, producing nectar and blue pollen from July to the end of August

In the evening when the bees have stopped flying, take off the roof and crownboard and make one or two pin holes in the newspaper. The queen excluder will keep the newspaper in place. Then gently lift the other brood box and its crownboard, with feed holes covered, off its floor and place it on top of the queen excluder and newspaper. Place the roof on top and leave well alone for about a week.

After a week you can check that all is well and that the queen is laying. You can rearrange the combs with brood into the box with the queen. This is a good opportunity to take out some of the older combs. Any surplus drawn combs in good condition can be sterilised with 80% acetic acid and stored carefully for re-use later.

Jobs to do in August

- finish taking off the honey early in the month
- check condition and siting of the hive and stand. Repair if needed
- check that the bees still have enough food reserves
- give the bees a stimulative feed of sugar syrup
- carry out a thorough inspection for disease
- unite any small colonies
- apply any treatment needed to control the population of varroa mites
- protect the clean dry supers from wax moth and store for next season.

Nick Withers

8 SEPTEMBER

You have made a good start with preparing your colonies for winter if you have been able to make sure your colonies are strong and healthy with plenty of young bees, have a young queen not more than two years old and are housed in a sound hive. There is still time to finish off any of these jobs if you did not manage to complete them in August.

The preparations for winter continue through this month by making sure that the bees have enough food. The treatment to reduce the population of the varroa mite continues to be an important part of your winter preparations.

COLONY ACTIVITY

The fall in the adult population slows down as younger bees replace the hard-worked foragers. The queen's egg-laying rate may increase in response to the autumn nectar flow from, for example, Michaelmas daisy, Himalayan balsam and ivy.

This is a critical time for untreated colonies as the varroa mite population continues to increase at the same time as the population of bees and brood is falling.

The drones in most colonies have been evicted. If you see drones still in the hive it may be because there may be some concern about the queen or that the colony is preparing to supersede her.

HELPING THE COLONY

Preparing for winter

One of the main causes of colony losses during the winter is starvation. To survive through the winter a colony of bees needs enough food in the hive to cover the period from October to the beginning of April. Sometimes the colony runs out of food because not enough stores were put away. This is usually due to negligence on the part of the beekeeper and can easily be avoided by topping up the stores in plenty of time.

Autumn forage

In some areas there may be useful forage available from late summer and autumn flowers. These can add to the stores for winter but the weather may turn out to be too cold or wet for the bees to go outside, so you should not depend on this source.

How much sugar syrup?

How much sugar syrup is needed of course depends on how much honey is already in the hive. Other factors are colony size, size of hive and the winter weather and length. There will be wide variations in different parts of the country.

The strain of bee is also a factor. For example, the Italian honey bee (*Apis mellifera ligustica*), many imported from New Zealand, will carry on converting food into brood instead of storing it, well into the autumn. The dark European honey bee (*Apis mellifera mellifera*), also referred to as the native British bee, is more frugal than the Italian bee. Our local bees, though now much hybridised by imported bees, are usually better adapted to our climate than imported strains.

I keep local bees in National hives on the North Downs in the south east of England and I have found that 18 kg of stores by the end of September will see the colony through to the following year. Usually there is plenty of food left in the spring and some combs full of stores have to be removed to make room for the queen to lay. Your minimum aim should be 18 kg. More is better than less so be generous with autumn feeding. The surplus combs of food in the spring are not wasted. They can be stored and used for emergency feeding or given to a nucleus in the summer. Some beekeepers say that more than 18 kg of stores is needed at the start of winter, so have a word with beekeepers in your locality and follow their advice.

How much honey is in the hive?

Before you start autumn feeding you need to estimate how much honey is in the hive already so that you can calculate how much sugar syrup is needed to top up. Experienced beekeepers can estimate stores by hefting. This is simply gently lifting the side of the hive just off the stand and estimating the weight by feel. Some beekeepers use a spring balance to lift the hive. You need to heft on both sides because the stores may be concentrated on one side.

You can gain experience of hefting by first of all estimating the amount of stores in the hive by looking at each comb and then hefting the hive. As you develop experience so in future you will be able to rely on hefting alone.

Sugar syrup

You should use only white granulated sugar, mixing 1 kg with 625 ml water. A simple way to mix the sugar and water is to pour the sugar into a suitable container, level the surface and add hot water to the same level. The mixture should then be stirred until all the sugar crystals are dissolved. Allow the sugar syrup to cool before delivering it to the bees.

Some beekeepers prefer cane sugar instead of beet sugar but I have found no difference. Do not use raw or brown sugar because this can result in dysentery in the spring, showing up as brown streaks near the hive entrance and on the frames. This will help to spread disease if the colony is suffering from nosema.

Example: How much sugar syrup?

First, find out how much honey is on each frame. This way you end up with an estimate of the equivalent number of full combs. A full National brood frame covered on both sides holds about 2.3 kg of honey. To calculate the quantity of sugar needed remember that 1 kg of sugar when made up to a syrup with water is equivalent to 1.25 kg of honey.

Estimated equivalent full frames of honey:		=	4.8
Estimated weight of honey in the hive:	4.8 x 2.3	=	11 kg
Honey equivalent needed to top up to 18 kg:	18 - 11	=	7 kg
Sugar needed (minimum):	7 ÷ 1.25	=	5.6 kg

A litre of sugar syrup contains about 0.73 kg of sugar so in the example you will need to top up the hive with 5.6/0.73 = 7.7 litres sugar syrup. So be generous and round it up to 8 litres.

FEEDERS

Contact feeders

This 'contact' feeder holds five litres of sugar syrup

A contact feeder has perforations or a mesh in the lid and is inverted and placed over the feed hole. The bees suck the sugar syrup through the perforations. These feeders range in size, the largest having a capacity of five litres.

After filling and replacing the airtight lid you should invert the feeder over a container to catch the small quantity of sugar syrup that will leak out until a partial vacuum is formed. This avoids soaking the bees in sugar syrup. Place the inverted feeder over the feed hole, add an empty super and replace the roof. The bees usually take down five litres of sugar syrup in four or five days.

If you need to refill the feeder you should wear a veil and light the smoker. You do not have to take off the crownboard but as soon as you take off the feeder the bees emerge quickly through the feed hole. Sometimes they are not pleased with your presence and a little smoke is needed to get them back beneath the crownboard before you replace the re-filled feeder.

Rapid feeders

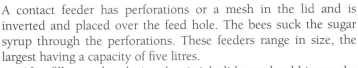

This round plastic 'rapid' feeder needs frequent topping up, which can be done without exposing the bees

A rapid feeder is one where the bees come up through a covered central tube. It is easy to fill and to place over the feed hole in the crownboard. It can be topped up without exposing the bees.

The bees can take the syrup down from a rapid feeder more quickly than from a contact feeder. The largest round plastic rapid feeders hold one litre of sugar syrup and the bees can take this down in about a day. It may need re-filling daily but this is easily done without exposing the bees and is convenient if you keep one or two stocks in your home garden.

If you keep your bees in an out-apiary, a Miller or Ashforth feeder may be worth considering. These are made of wood or plastic and have external dimensions so that the feeder covers the hive. They will hold up to 10 litres of sugar syrup, so reducing the number of visits to the apiary.

The bees reach the syrup through a central channel in the Miller feeder and a channel on one side in the Ashforth. If you keep your bees on a solid floor you may have your hive tipped slightly towards the entrance so that moisture collecting on the floor runs out of the hive. The Ashforth feeder should be placed on the hive with the bees' access at the front so that they can take all the syrup.

The Miller feeder should be positioned so that the central access runs from the back to the front of the hive but may have to be turned through 90 degrees for the bees to take the last few drops of syrup if the hive is on a slight slope. The colony can take all the sugar syrup down in two or three days.

After filling the feeders don't forget to let the bees know there is food above them. Simply dribble a little sugar syrup through their access channel and they will soon get the message.

If the weather turns cold and the temperature falls below 14°C, the bees will start to cluster and will not leave the brood box to enter the feeders. This means that you should start feeding during the first week of September and complete it before the end of September. This allows the bees time to process the sugar syrup and to store it in the right place. Stores with too much water can ferment, which is harmful to the bees. Stores in the wrong place for the bees add to the risk of isolation starvation.

These Ashforth (left) and Miller (right) feeders hold about 10 litres. They are useful for reducing travelling to top up in an out-apiary

Check the weight

After you have completed the topping up, do check that the food has been stored. There is no need to open the colony to examine each comb; you can check the weight by hefting. A hive with 18 kg or more of stores will feel as if it is nailed to the hive stand!

Remove the queen excluder

The queen excluder should be removed, cleaned and stored ready for next spring. If you are wintering your bees on two deep brood chambers or a deep and a shallow, the queen may become isolated beneath the excluder as the cluster moves up through the food.

Avoid a robbing spree

As soon as the bees discover there is a reservoir of food above them they tell their sisters by means of the round dance. The message the bees receive is that there is a good supply of food nearby and they go outside to search. As well as creating a lot of excitement in the apiary, the searching bees may find a fault in another hive, or a poorly defended colony, and start a robbing spree.

You can avoid this problem by giving the first feed in the evening when the bees have stopped flying. The bees will not fly out if it is

Chris Jackson

Michaelmas daisies produce yellow pollen, providing useful forage for bees when there is little else available

dark and instead will search inside the hive. The excitement soon dies down. You can top up or refill the feeder at any time of day.

Other precautions to reduce the risk of robbing are to start feeding all the colonies in the apiary at the same time and be sure not to spill any sugar syrup on the ground or on the hives. All entrances should be small so that they are easily defended.

Varroa control and feeding

In August I suggested that you should treat your bees with Apiguard to control the varroa mite. The instructions state it should be applied after the honey has been removed and not used when the maximum daily temperature is below 15°C.

This means the treatment should be applied from mid August to the end of September. The recommendation on the Apiguard leaflet and website (www.vita-europe.com) is not to apply Apiguard whilst feeding in case the bees spend all their time taking the feed and not bothering to clean out the Apiguard gel.

The best time to top up food for winter stores is from the first week in September when the bees have become accustomed to the odour of thymol, the active ingredient in Apiguard.

During the last two or three weeks of the six-week Apiguard treatment, the remaining gel in the Apiguard trays usually dries out and is ignored by the bees. I remove the Apiguard tray and smear the remaining dry gel on a piece of card and place this on the top bars to one side of the feed hole in the crownboard. The usual bee space between the top bars and crownboard is adequate for access by the bees to the card, so the eke can now be removed. The food in a contact feeder is then placed above the feed hole in the crownboard. In my out-apiaries the card with the dry gel is placed in the centre on the top bars and the Ashforth and Miller feeders are used as normal.

Jobs to do in September

- examine each comb to find out how much honey is stored
- learn to estimate the stores in the hive by hefting
- top up the stores in the hive to a minimum of 18 kg
- check that the bees have stored the food by hefting the hive after feeding
- remove the queen excluder, clean and store for next season
- remove the empty Apiguard trays or other varroa treatment.

9 OCTOBER

The beekeeper's work is beginning to wind down in October but there are still a few important jobs to be done in the apiary. The hive, containing a good store of food and bees, is a tempting source of protein for other animals. So the hive needs to be protected from predators. Another job is to clean and sterilise spare equipment ready to use next year.

October is the time for many honey shows when some beekeepers show their honey in competitions locally and at the National Honey Show. As well as the honey competitions, there are many events with interesting lectures and a programme of workshops where beginners can learn more about bees and try their hand at a variety of skills such as making mead and beeswax candles, and painting with wax.

COLONY ACTIVITY

Most of the bees in the hive are now the longer-lived winter bees. Many will survive through to early April. During warm days the bees will collect nectar and pollen from ivy. During cold wet periods the bees will start eating the food stores.

When the temperature falls below 18°C the bees start to cluster by gathering closer together in the brood area to maintain the required temperature at around 35°C.

HELPING THE COLONY

Preparing for winter

During August you started preparing for winter by making sure your hives were sound with strong healthy colonies and young queens. In September you made sure that the colony had enough food stores to last through to the beginning of April next year.

The hive of bees with its store of food is also attractive to other wildlife. During the active season the colony is able to defend itself. In the cold weather the bees cluster and so cannot protect themselves and their food store. This month, therefore, one of the main jobs is to protect the hive from other animals looking for food and shelter.

A mouse will enter a hive to nest for the winter. It can damage comb and frames and the cluster is disturbed throughout the winter

Mice

As the cold nights start, mice will look for a warm dry corner to nest. A hive is ideal with the added bonus of plenty of food to hand. When the bees are in a cluster a mouse can simply walk into an unprotected hive. It can make a nasty mess and destroy combs and frames, and the smell is objectionable to bees as well as to humans. Usually the cluster will be disturbed throughout the winter and the colony will be seriously weakened and sometimes die out.

You can easily prevent a mouse entering the hive by using a narrow entrance or fitting a mouseguard. Beekeepers using solid floors may want to maintain a wide entrance to help with hive ventilation. In this case a mouseguard should be fitted as soon as the frosty nights start.

If October is still warm, the bees are likely to be gathering late autumn pollen and this can easily be scraped off their legs as they enter through the holes of the mouseguard. The valuable early spring pollen can be lost in the same way. I suggest you delay fitting the mouseguard until the pollen gathering is finished. It is worth while checking that a mouse has not already entered the hive as you fit the mouseguard.

One of the advantages of the open mesh floor is that it provides plenty of hive ventilation, so you can maintain a narrow entrance all the time. An entrance of not more than 8 mm high will stop a mouse entering the hive and bees can enter without losing their load of pollen.

Woodpeckers

Margaret Cowley

This beautiful green woodpecker can seriously damage a beehive and destroy the colony

I kept bees for many years before our local green woodpeckers discovered that a beehive is full of their favourite food. When there is a very heavy frost and the woodpeckers can no longer dig for ants they find that hives are a soft target. Once this has been discovered the birds pass the information around the local woodpecker population very quickly.

They can cause considerable damage to hives, hammering 70 mm holes in the sides or roofs. After the woodpecker's meal, any surviving bees have been badly disturbed and become disoriented. If your bees are in an out-apiary or you did not find the damage to the hive straight away, the woodpecker will be back to do more damage and rats may finish the job, completely destroying the hive and contents.

You can prevent the woodpecker attacking by covering your hive with wire netting or plastic strips. I have found that the 25 mm wire netting is the easiest to handle and gives good protection. It is best to wrap the wire netting loosely around the hive to prevent the birds getting a firm foothold. I raise the netting a little above the entrance so that the bees can land near the entrance without having to negotiate the wires.

I have experienced a stack of supers stored outside being damaged by woodpeckers. It seems that once the woodpecker has discovered that hives contain food they are tempted by anything the looks like a hive. So protection for empty supers stored outside is also advisable.

This hive is protected from the green woodpecker. The small entrance no more than 8 mm high will prevent a mouse from entering

Wasps

Wasps will still be trying their luck at entering the hive until the first frosts kill their nest. A strong colony and a small entrance will usually keep them out.

Badgers

Badgers occasionally interfere with hives

Sometimes you will see muddy claw marks left by badgers on a hive. They rarely cause any damage to hives in this country but can be a nuisance burrowing near the hive. It may be that the weight of the hive in winter and its being raised off the ground provides enough protection from the badger. Placing the hive on a paving slab and roping and pegging the hive to the ground in winter is a solution if necessary.

My home apiary is within about 50 metres of a large sett and badgers nightly jog along their track through the apiary. They have never attacked a hive but once they did tip over two nucleus hives that were being over-wintered. They have also taken the contents of mini queen-mating hives in summer time. So if you are planning to take a nucleus through the winter, make sure it is raised from the ground and securely strapped and pegged. I now use a full size brood box with a divider to form twin nucleus hives for over-wintering without trouble from badgers.

This nucleus hive was tipped over by badgers. One frame was found near the sett. The remaining bees and queen survived the ordeal

Ivy

Ivy flowers in late September through to December and is probably the last source of nectar and pollen for honey bees during the year. Ivy produces large quantities of nectar and sometimes the honey can be extracted. It has an unusual taste and some people, probably a minority, like it. The uncertain October weather and the timing for the autumn treatment for varroa make it difficult to plan for harvesting ivy honey. If the bees are able to forage, it provides a useful boost to the winter stores, especially pollen.

Ivy nectar contains more glucose than fructose so it crystallises very quickly. Some beekeepers say that this can cause problems for the bees when it is used for winter stores. I have never experienced any problems perhaps because ivy honey has never provided for all the winter requirements for my colonies. I always top up the stores with sugar syrup to about 18 kg by the end of September and any additional stores available after this are a bonus for the bees.

Killianwoods / Wikimedia Commons

Cleaning and storing equipment

October is a good time to clean and sterilise spare equipment before storing it away ready for next season. It may be tempting to stack it away out of sight before cleaning and sterilising as there are so many other things to do. It is very frustrating to find it dirty and perhaps damaged by vermin when you need it in the spring. Cleaning out the storage area or shed and getting rid of old or damaged equipment will help to control mice and keep your stored equipment in good order.

Brood comb

Used brood comb can carry pathogens. To help maintain the health of your colony all brood combs need to be replaced every two or three years. Clean combs in good condition can be stored and reused after being sterilised.

Old dark brown or misshapen comb or comb with patches of drone cells should not be reused. Some beekeepers simply burn used brood frames and comb and replace them with new frames and foundation. There is little wax that can be recovered from used brood frames and immediate burning reduces the risk of disease. The safest practice is to wrap the unwanted frames and comb in newspaper and burn them as soon as you have removed them from the hive This reduces the risk of bees finding them and scavenging the remains of honey and perhaps disease pathogens.

Hive parts

Spare hive parts such as brood boxes, floors and crownboards should be cleaned and sterilised before storing them away for the winter. This also applies to second-hand equipment because you do not know what diseases it may have harboured.

All the wooden parts should first be scraped clean of burr or brace comb and propolis. The wood is then scorched with a blow lamp until it becomes a uniform coffee-brown colour. You should, of course, avoid setting the wood alight. Take care to scorch any cracks or crevices and the corners that may conceal the spores of bee diseases.

Hot washing soda can be used to clean equipment such as queen excluders and open mesh floors. Place them on a flat surface and use a scrubbing brush after scraping off any wax and propolis.

Small items such as Porter bee escapes and spacers can be soaked in washing soda. Always wear kitchen washing-up gloves to protect your hands when using washing soda.

Bee suit and veil

At the end of the season you should wash your bee suit and veil following the manufacturer's instructions. It is good practice to wash bee suits and veils regularly throughout the active season. They may not appear soiled but dried bee venom surely does nothing to encourage docility in the bees!

All that is needed during the season is an occasional overnight soak in washing soda. During the winter you should keep your overalls and veil in a warm dry place otherwise in the spring they will be soiled with black mould.

Hive ventilation

During the winter, as the bees in the cluster consume honey, water vapour is given off, being the product of metabolism. Bees maintain the cluster temperature but they do not heat the inside of the hive. The moisture-carrying capacity of cold air is limited so additional ventilation is needed to remove the excess water vapour. If moisture builds up inside the hive, moulds will grow and sometimes can be seen on the combs near the walls of the hive. Damp conditions in the hive are more harmful to bees than cold, so it is important to make sure that there is enough ventilation during the winter.

Open mesh floors provide sufficient ventilation but make sure that the area underneath is clear to allow a good flow of air underneath and around the hive.

Beekeepers using solid floors provide additional ventilation by using matchsticks or something similar, to lift the crownboard a few millimetres to allow air to flow out from the brood area. The bees sometimes fill the gap with propolis so I suggest you do this job after the cluster is well established. It will be worth while checking later in the winter that the gap is still there. It is advisable to keep the feed hole closed in the winter as an open hole in the centre may create a draught through the centre of the cluster. The entrance block should be removed to make a wide entrance to allow enough air to enter the brood area.

A layer of insulation above the crownboard will help to prevent condensation forming underneath the crownboard and dropping on to the cluster. This will be especially useful with glass crownboards.

Sterilising brood comb

Fumes from 80% acetic acid will destroy the spores of the fairly common diseases nosema and chalkbrood. Acetic acid sterilisation will also deal with the wax moth, which is particularly attracted to stored brood comb. Acetic acid fumes will not kill the spores of American Foul Brood (AFB), a notifiable disease in this country. If you are not sure you are clear of AFB in your area, ask for advice from your local bee inspectors or an experienced beekeeper.

I use 80% acetic acid to sterilise brood combs from wax moth before storing them over winter. This treatment kills all stages of wax moth. The 80% strength acetic acid is available from the equipment suppliers. You should wear protective gloves and goggles when handling this strength acetic acid and it is highly corrosive to metal and will damage concrete.

The brood boxes and frames should be scraped clean of propolis and bits of brace and burr wax and you should remove any metal parts. The metal runners should be smeared with petroleum jelly. The brood box and combs can be placed on a wooden board such as a crownboard with the feed holes closed up. Place an absorbent pad in a shallow plastic tray on top of the brood box and pour about 140 ml of 80% acetic acid on to the pad. Place a wooden board on top of the brood box and seal up the joints with tape or enclose it in a plastic bag such as a large 'wheely' bin bag. Leave it alone for at least a week for the heavy fumes to sterilise the combs. If you have more than one brood box they may be stacked and 140 ml 80% acetic acid poured on a pad above each box.

Recycling frames

Used frames can be recycled by being cleaned and fitted with new foundation. This may entail storing the used combs until you have all the combs you want to replace. Make sure you keep them in a bee-tight container until you are ready to do the job.

The wax combs should be removed from the frames by first removing the wedge from the top bar. The comb can then be removed in one piece, using a hive tool to ease it from the bottom bar. The wax comb may now be wrapped in newspaper and burnt to eliminate any harboured disease.

The remaining wax and propolis should now be scraped from the frames. Give special attention to cleaning the grooves in the side bars and the gap between the bottom bars so that you can easily slide in the new foundation. A swan-necked frame cleaning tool, available from equipment suppliers, is a great help to cleaning out the grooves in the side bars.

You can make the cleaning job a bit easier if you place the used brood frame with the comb in a solar wax melter. Of course you have to do this in the summer time. I place the frames on a drip screen to allow a small gap between the floor of the solar wax extractor tray and the comb. This makes it easier to remove the frames and debris after the wax has been melted out of the comb. Scraping the frames clean is now a much easier job which you can do at any convenient time later in the year. The 45–50 g of recovered wax per brood frame is a bonus. The debris can be added to your compost heap or burnt.

Another optional refinement is to soak the frames for about five minutes in a very hot solution of washing soda and water. The frames are much nicer to handle and all traces of wax and propolis are removed by this treatment. They can now be stored until the spring when the new foundation is fitted just before you need them.

Jobs to do in October

- complete topping up the food stores to about 18 kg if necessary
- if you have solid floors fit mouseguards and wide entrances for ventilation
- fit wire netting or plastic strips around the hive to deter woodpeckers
- clean, sterilise and store spare equipment.

10 NOVEMBER

There is little beekeeping work to be done in the apiary this month. An occasional visit, especially after a storm or snowfall, to check that everything is in order is usually all that is needed. You can enjoy the feeling that you have done your best to help the bees to survive the winter.

Indoors there is still plenty to be done. Perhaps you will have time to prepare your first batch of soft-set and clear honey from your store of crystallised honey, ready to give away as gifts. You may still have some equipment that needs to be cleaned and sterilised ready for the spring. This is a good time, too, to clean up all the bits of beeswax you saved during the summer.

Ivy

Claire Waring

COLONY ACTIVITY

Everything in the hive is very quiet now. There is little pollen or nectar available outside so there is very little opportunity for foraging. Bees will still fly out occasionally in reasonable weather to get rid of waste products and to remove the corpses of dead bees.

Egg-laying practically ceases and the population continues to fall. The long-lived winter bees have replaced the harder-worked summer bees. Food consumption is at a minimum as there is little if any brood-rearing and practically no work to be done. The winter cluster will be broken during warm spells or if the colony is disturbed by the beekeeper or predators.

The varroa mites surviving the autumn treatment will continue to reproduce in cells with brood and as there is little brood and only occasional bouts of egg-laying at this time a few mites will occupy a relatively large proportion of brood cells. So the population of varroa mite is still increasing while the population of bees is decreasing.

THE WINTER CLUSTER

The honey bee is cold-blooded so its body adopts the ambient temperature of its environment and it has no system of temperature control as do warm-blooded animals. Bees can raise body temperature by muscular action of the wing muscles, in other words, shivering. They can also keep their body temperature up as they fly, so bees can fly outside the hive for short periods even when the temperature is below freezing.

If the bee's body temperature falls below about 18°C they are unable to exercise their wing muscles. Bees become immobile when their body temperature falls below about 10°C and eventually they will die.

As the outside temperature falls below 18°C, the bees begin to gather closer together to form a cluster. The cluster forms around the queen and any brood still in the colony. Part of the cluster will be in contact with the food stores. As the outside temperature drops, the cluster contracts and, below about 14°C, it is fully formed. The ball of bees has a compact outer shell of quiet, still bees and an inner core where the bees can move about. The shell is made up of a few layers of bees with their heads facing into the core; the abdomens are on the outside where the stings are ready to protect the core if necessary.

The bees in the middle of the cluster generate the heat by eating honey and exercising their wing muscles. Those on the outer layers form a good layer of insulation to reduce heat loss from the cluster. There is a constant gentle movement of bees taking their turn as heat generators and insulators. The cluster expands or contracts to maintain the cluster temperature when the ambient temperature varies. So the bees regulate the temperature within the cluster, not the temperature in the hive.

The loss of heat from the cluster can be controlled by the expansion or contraction of the cluster. The temperature in the brood area is maintained at 34–35°C. The larvae also contribute some heat as they consume food. During broodless periods the temperature inside the cluster is maintained between 20 and 30°C so that the temperature on the outside layer is kept above about 10°C throughout the cold periods. If the temperature on the outermost layer of the cluster falls below 10°C the bees become immobilised, drop off the cluster and die.

HELPING THE COLONY

Varroa control

There will be an opportunity to reduce the population of varroa during December so it is worth while monitoring the varroa population towards the end of the month. Monitoring during cold weather when the colony is in a cluster can be unreliable, so choose a time when the cluster is broken during warmer periods and keep the inserts in position for at least seven days. At this time of the year an average mite drop of one per day represents about 150 mites in the colony. Anything we can do to reduce even a very low infestation is worth while.

Jobs to do in November

- monitor natural mite drop and plan further treatment for varroa if needed
- check that the hive and protection against predators is intact after windy weather
- check that the entrance is not blocked by snow or debris such as dead bees
- complete cleaning, sterilising and storing spare equipment.

Nick Withers

Ivy provides the last chance for the bees to top up their winter stores. It can yield nectar and orangey-yellow pollen from late September to late December. You can see the bee's extended tongue sucking up the nectar

11 DECEMBER

All is quiet in the apiary in December. There is little work for the beekeeper beyond making sure that hives are intact after storms and entrances are clear after snow. There is another opportunity to do something to keep the varroa mite population at the lowest level ready for the expansion of brood-rearing.

This is the time to reflect on the past year's beekeeping and think about how you will develop your beekeeping next year. Perhaps you are ready to take the BBKA's Basic Assessment. As you develop the skills to manage and learn more about the honey bee, each year you will get even more enjoyment and pleasure from the craft.

COLONY ACTIVITY

Even on quite cold days with bright sunshine the bees will fly outside for cleansing flights and perhaps to collect water though there is usually little need for extra water to dilute stores as yet. There may be very limited bouts of egg-laying during any spells of mild weather and the population will continue to drift downwards.

With no brood-rearing, little activity and minimum heat loss very little food is consumed. At the end of December, as more daylight hours stimulate the queen to start egg-laying, food consumption will start to increase again.

HELPING THE COLONY

Varroa control

The varroa population is usually fairly low after the autumn treatment. However, the number of mites is still growing and if left unchecked a few can damage the small amount of new brood as soon as the queen starts to increase her egg-laying at the end of this month. Keeping the mite population as low as possible during the winter will help to give the young brood in the spring the best chance to thrive.

Many beekeepers now use lactic or oxalic acid treatment in winter to reduce the varroa population. The legal position about acid treatment is rather involved but it is now widely used as a winter treatment in this country. I would advise that before you go ahead with trickling oxalic acid or spraying lactic acid on your bees you should discuss it with your bee inspector or an experienced beekeeper.

The best time to use lactic or oxalic acid treatment to kill the varroa mites is when there is no brood in the colony, so all the mites are exposed on the adult bees. The acid will not penetrate wax so it does not kill the varroa mites on bee pupae in sealed cells. Usually in December there is very little or no brood in the colony.

I find that trickling oxalic acid is much simpler than spraying lactic acid. Lactic acid is potentially less hazardous and the treatment can be repeated if necessary. You should only use the oxalic acid treatment once on a colony during the winter.

Oxalic acid treatment

Choose a still dry day when the temperature is between 3 and 7°C and use a lukewarm mixture to avoid chilling the bees. Remove the roof and crownboard and trickle 5 ml of 3.2% oxalic acid mixture on each 'seam' of bees. Do not overdose. You may find a torch handy to be able to see the seams where the cluster is low down in the brood chamber.

Be very careful when using oxalic acid. It can be harmful to bees and humans and is corrosive. I recommend that you use only the ready-mixed 3.2% oxalic acid and sugar syrup available in a 100 ml container with 5 ml dispensing chamber. This is enough to treat up to three colonies. Buy an empty container as well, to practise trickling 5 ml of water before trickling the oxalic acid mixture on the bees.

You should give only one treatment during the winter and take care not to overdose. Put on your bee suit and veil, wear gloves and goggles and follow the supplier's instructions carefully.

Trickling 3.2% oxalic acid on a dry, still, cold day to control the varroa population. Keep the dispensing chamber uppermost

Geoff close

Lactic acid treatment

A 15% solution of lactic acid in water is sprayed lightly on each side of a brood comb covered with bees using a hand-held fine mist sprayer. The bees take on a grey appearance when the correct dose has been applied. If the bees appear black too much of the solution has been used. The dose is 5 ml on each side of the frame. Before you start find out how many 'squirts' of the sprayer will give you 5 ml. This treatment is applied two or three times at three-day intervals.

Applying the treatment is much easier if you can work with another beekeeper. If you are working on your own you may find it easier to use a 'frame grip' to hold the frame with one hand and spray with the other.

REFLECT ON THE YEAR'S BEEKEEPING

As you look back on the year's beekeeping, make a note of all the aspects that went well and those that you consider could be improved. Here are some of the points to consider:

- providing enough space for bees and the queen to lay in the spring
- finding the queen
- adding supers in time
- monitoring varroa population and treatment
- harvesting
- recognising healthy brood
- swarm control
- did you have all the equipment you needed?

Jobs to do in December

- check that the hive and protection against predators is intact
- check that the hive entrance is kept clear of snow and debris
- apply lactic or oxalic acid treatment during a broodless period
- reflect on your beekeeping during the past year
- plan to improve basic skills and learn more advanced beekeeping next year
- get a copy of the syllabus and entry form for the BBKA Basic Assessment.

12 JANUARY

At first glance, a beehive in January appears lifeless but there is a lot of interesting activity going on inside the hive.

If you have not yet completed the cleaning of spare equipment it is not too late to do it this month but the best time is as soon as possible after the equipment is taken out of use. General cleanliness and hygiene of equipment and the storage area are essential ingredients in maintaining colony health and well-being.

An apiary in winter. Keep the entrances clear of snow so bees can take cleansing flights

COLONY ACTIVITY

During the autumn egg-laying dwindled; consequently there was little brood-rearing and also little foraging, resulting in minimum food consumption. The increasing length of January days helps to trigger increased egg-laying so a higher temperature is needed and maintained in the brood area. This, along with the increasing requirement to feed larvae, results in increasing consumption of stores throughout the month.

On fine sunny days bees will fly out of the hive for cleansing flights and later in the month to collect water to dilute stores. During a mild winter towards the end of the month perhaps we will enjoy seeing bees bringing brightly coloured pollen loads into the hive collected from winter flowers such as hellebores and mahonia. Spring will soon be here!

HELPING THE COLONY

January is probably the month when there is very little work to do directly with the bees and therefore it is a good month to start studying and planning for the spring.

If you have bees already, have a look at the hives every couple of weeks and after stormy weather, to make sure that the hives are intact with roofs secure. Check that there are no signs of woodpecker attack, that mouse guards have not been disturbed and that the apiary fencing is secure. Clear the hive entrance if it is blocked by snow. Check that the entrance is not blocked by debris or dead bees.

During January many beginners worry about their bees, like new parents worrying about every little snuffle at night from their new baby. Are the bees still alive? Have a look at the entrance on a fine sunny day and you should see bees taking cleansing flights or starting to forage for pollen.

Is there enough food?

If you provided your bees with 18 kg or more of stores in the autumn, there should still be plenty in the hive. The bees consume only very small amounts of stores when brood-rearing is minimal until the end of December, but brood-rearing and consumption of stores increases during January. If you are concerned you could check by 'hefting' the hive.

Emergency feeding

The best practice is to give the colony plenty of food before the end of September to last through to April without resorting to emergency feeding during the winter. Sometimes even when you made sure your colony had plenty of stores in the autumn the bees are still short of stores. Perhaps the over-wintered colony was large, with not enough space in the brood chamber for food. Perhaps the winter was unusually mild resulting in early brood-rearing. Whatever the reason, if the bees are short of stores during the winter then of course providing emergency food is better than letting the bees starve to death.

Feeding the bees in winter with sugar syrup may cause some excitement and disturb the cluster, upsetting the regulation of temperature and humidity. Also the additional water in the syrup increases the risk of dysentery. Beekeepers usually use home-made candy or bakers' fondant, or a bag of white granulated sugar.

Any food you give the bees in winter should be placed in contact with the cluster. Individual bees are unable to leave the cluster when the temperature is below about 6°C. So if you can see the bees underneath the feed hole you can place the bag of sugar or fondant over the feed hole on top of the crownboard. If you cannot see the bees through the feed hole, the cluster is to one side and you should place the food underneath the crownboard directly on the top of the frames and in contact with the cluster.

Bees will bring in water, or if they are unable to fly out they will use their saliva to add to solid fondant or sugar so that they can take up the food. The bag of sugar is moistened, otherwise the granulated sugar will run into the hive. When presented with dry granulated sugar they do not appear to recognise it as food and throw it out of the hive to form a neat pile of sugar in front of the entrance.

My method is to pour about 120 ml water into a 1 kg bag of white granulated sugar and let the water soak into the sugar for a day or two. When it is set remove the paper from one side and place the bag with the exposed sugar in contact with the cluster. You will need an eke or an empty super so that you can replace the cover board and roof.

Snowdrops are a welcome source of good quality brownish-yellow pollen from January to March, available when the weather is suitable for bees to fly

Nick Withers

Do not disturb

There is always a temptation to have a quick look in the hive. This can result in breaking the cluster, which upsets temperature and humidity regulation, so it's best not to disturb the bees if you can avoid it.

If there is no sign of life then it may be useful to investigate. On a fine sunny day with your veil on, gently remove the woodpecker guard, roof and cover board. This may be enough to reassure you. If necessary you can remove frames near the hive wall without disturbing the cluster to have a closer look.

If you find the bees are dead, close up the entrance to prevent access by other bees and leave everything as it is. Ask your bee inspector or other experienced beekeeper for advice. There are several possible causes, and you should try with some local help to establish the reason for the loss. Perhaps you will learn something useful that you can correct in your winter preparations for next season. Some losses, however, are beyond the control of the beekeeper.

Jobs to do in January

- check that the hive and protection against predators is intact especially after high winds
- check that the hive entrance is kept clear of snow and debris
- check food stores.

13 FEBRUARY

Preparations for the new season begin in earnest this month. The queen increases her egg-laying and the winter bees can be busy foraging on those few warm February days. There is little the beekeeper can do with the bees but there is plenty of preparation by the bees in readiness for the active season.

COLONY ACTIVITY

On cold days in February everything looks very quiet in the apiary but quite a lot is happening inside the cluster. The empty cells in the middle of the cluster are being prepared for eggs and the queen starts laying, slowly at first in January and at an increasing rate through this month. As egg-laying increases so does food consumption. More food is needed to maintain the higher temperature in the growing brood area and to feed the increasing number of larvae.

During the first part of the winter, when there is very little for the bees to do, they do not eat much food but now the consumption may increase four-fold. This is the time when we will find out if our preparations in the autumn were good enough.

Those nice warm sunny days in February will tempt the bees out to forage for nectar and pollen from nearby winter flowers such as mahonia, hellebores, snowdrops and crocus. An early-flowering willow tree will provide masses of pollen. The bees will also get rid of the indigestible waste that has been stored in their digestive systems during prolonged poor weather when they were unable to leave the hive. Let's hope that the bees do not deposit their waste on your neighbour's washing or car! It washes off quite easily but may still be upsetting.

February sees the start of the most testing time of the year for bees. The winter bees are now quite old in bee life terms. They have to work harder than ever feeding an increasing number of larvae, foraging as the weather improves and maintaining the higher temperature for a growing brood area. Many of the older bees will die so don't be surprised or alarmed to find a few dead bees outside the entrance.

Bees enjoy collecting water from a wet board warmed by sunshine

HELPING THE COLONY

Is there enough food?

Check the food stores by hefting the hive. You should provide some emergency feeding if the colony is at risk of running out of food. I suggest you provide a bag of sugar or fondant. If the weather is mild and the bees are flying out regularly, later in the month you may feed with sugar syrup using a contact feeder placed directly over the cluster. You can add insulation over the top of the frames and around the feeder. This will help to maintain the temperature of the sugar syrup when the temperature falls at night.

Isolation starvation

The bees can also starve even when there is plenty of food in the hive. This is known as 'isolation starvation'. The bees consume stores in contact with the cluster. In prolonged cold weather they may reach the top of the stores and are unable to move sideways across a gap to ample stores on one side of the hive. If the weather suddenly gets cold after a short spell of warm weather the cluster can form again out of reach of stores. So not only do they need enough stores, but the stores need to be in the right place above the cluster. Perhaps the colony was too small, or the weather was simply too cold for too long. All the beekeeper can do to reduce the risk of isolation starvation is to provide enough sugar syrup at the right time.

The tassels of the hazel are conspicuous from late January to early March. The flowers are wind-pollinated, but in suitable foraging weather bees will collect the light yellow pollen from bushes near the apiary

Jobs to do in February

- check the stores by hefting the hive and, if necessary, providing emergency food
- check that the hives have not been disturbed by animals and high winds and that the mouse and woodpecker protection is still intact
- make sure the entrance is kept clear of debris, snow and dead bees
- carry on studying bees and beekeeping
- start collecting and preparing the equipment you will need in the coming season.

14 MARCH

The start of spring brings new life to plants and bees and a feeling of wonder and anticipation to beekeepers. But there are often times when early spring reverts to a wintry spell and this is especially testing for our bees. So much depends on the weather.

COLONY ACTIVITY

As the days lengthen and the weather warms up, the bees will become more active. The queen's egg-laying rate will increase, as will foraging on good days, and water collectors will be flying out to collect water to dilute winter food stores. All the many other activities that go on in the hive continue, such as preparing cells for eggs, feeding larvae, capping brood cells with wax, cleaning, and removing debris and corpses.

Towards the end of the month a few drone cells, which are slightly larger than worker cells, may be prepared by the bees. The queen will lay unfertilised eggs in these. The first drones will emerge 24 days later, usually later on in April. The weather will have a big impact on how the colony develops. A cold March will slow down the development and warm weather will speed things up.

March is the start of the most testing time of the year for bees. This month will see their food reserves at the lowest level when the demand for food is growing for brood-rearing. Increasing opportunities to forage and the need to bring in fresh pollen and water add to the work load and the consumption of food.

Most of the few remaining winter bees will die during this month. At first there is a fairly small force of young bees taking their place. As we move towards the end of the month, the brood population (eggs, larvae and pupae) is likely to be greater than that of the adult bees.

The weather

Poor weather can add to the bees' problems. March sometimes includes some lovely warm sunny periods, which encourage plants to thrive and flower early and bees to forge ahead producing more brood. That is fine if it goes on but sometimes these fine spells are followed by a sharp return to cold weather, causing the bees to

re-form the cluster. Fewer adult bees now have a larger brood area
to keep warm.

Usually the colony can cope and the result is simply a slow-down in its growth. In prolonged cold spells some of the brood
may be abandoned, be chilled and die. The colony usually recovers
as the weather improves.

Sometimes a colony may be at risk of starving even when there
is still food available in the hive. This is because the cluster may
re-form on part of the frames without stores of food and the bees
were unable to move to the food during the cold spell.

Watch the entrance

Before taking off the roof watch the entrance. Look for bees flying
straight out and making a 'beeline' in the direction of forage and
returning with pollen loads on their legs. This is a good sign that all
is well. It is not encouraging if there are no bees to be seen or they
are wandering about aimlessly on the front of the hive.

Light brown spots of excreta on the front of the hive may be
caused by the bees eating fermented stores, or being confined in the
hive by prolonged cold weather, or by too much water in the food.
If this is what you find, look for the same soiling on the combs
when you open the hive. Make a note to give syrup earlier in the
autumn next year to give your bees time to ripen it for storage.

It is a good sign when bees return with
pollen on a fine day in February or March

HELPING THE COLONY

Do they have enough food?

Check food reserves by hefting, that is by lifting the hive on both sides, one after the other, because the remaining food may all be concentrated on one side only. If they are short of food you can feed sugar syrup made by mixing 1 kg of white sugar to 625 ml of water.

Spring feeding

You may find that during cold spells the bees will not go up into the feeder to reach the syrup, so a contact or bucket feeder is better in the early spring as it can be placed directly over the cluster and the bees have access to the syrup without moving far from the cluster. A contact feeder needs some care when inverting it over the cluster or feed hole. Firstly you should fill it to within one or two cm of the top then, with the lid secured, invert it over a bucket to collect the syrup that runs out until a vacuum is created in the feeder.

Now you can place it over the cluster, or the feed hole if the cluster is directly underneath, without spilling syrup on to the colony. You may still find a small amount of syrup flooding on to the colony when the feeder is nearly empty and there is a sudden change in temperature, but this is soon cleared up by the bees.

Some books suggest that a more dilute syrup should be fed in the spring as a stimulative feed. The additional water content may be helpful to small colonies but too much water in the bees' gut can cause dysentery if they are confined in the hive for too long.

Early sources of pollen

By looking at the hive entrance you will be able to see if there is a good supply of early pollen available in your locality. On a fine day when the bees are flying freely, you will see the pollen loads on the foragers' hind legs as they return to the hive. If you happen to keep your bees where there is a dearth of early pollen, feeding pollen patties or pollen substitute may be worth while. I have never needed to feed pollen or a substitute and I believe that there are very few parts of this country that suffer from a shortage of early pollen. If you are in doubt, talk to someone at your local group.

Water supply

A nearby supply of clean water will help your colony to build up. The bees need water to dilute their stores of honey to meet their energy needs for foraging and to feed the increasing population of larvae.

The source of water seems to work well when it is about five metres or so from the hive, sheltered from wind and warmed by winter sunshine. Of course it must never be allowed to run dry as the bees will soon find another source that may be further away or in your neighbour's garden!

A container of peat, with holes in the bottom, kept moist in a slightly larger container of water, or a sloping piece of wood kept wet under the dripping tap of a water butt, both work well. The shallow edge of a garden pond or a water feature providing an area of constant damp stonework warmed by the sun will also attract the water collectors.

A quick inspection

Choose a warm sunny day when the bees are flying freely. A good guide for the timing of the first inspection is when the bees are visiting the flowers of the flowering currant. The air temperature should be 16°C or more for a quick inspection and this is likely later on in March. If the conditions are not right for opening the hive this month, wait until April.

Before opening the hive at any time it's a good idea to know beforehand the reason for disturbing the bees. Know what you are going to look for and what you will do, depending of course on what you find. Do be gentle but firm as you remove and replace hive parts or frames. Keep the hive open for the shortest time possible.

The purpose of a quick inspection in early spring is to find out if the colony is queenright, in other words if there is a healthy queen, if the colony is healthy and if there are any frames that need to be replaced at the next inspection. Just in case you suspect disease, have a matchbox handy in which you can collect a sample of bees for analysis.

Also do use a record book or card to note the condition of the colony so that you will be able to see progress and remind yourself of the previous condition before each regular inspection.

A clean or new floor

Make sure that you are well protected and check that your veil is secure and the zip is closed. The smoker should be producing cool smoke. Now you are ready to open the hive.

You may have over-wintered your bees on a single brood chamber, or a brood chamber and a super known as a brood and a half or perhaps on a double brood chamber, all without a queen excluder. If your hive has a solid floor it's a good idea to change the floor if you have a spare, or clean the one you have. Better still, replace it with an open mesh floor (OMF). This will help you to monitor and control the varroa mite population.

Take off the roof and other parts until you have only the box with bees and brood with the crownboard on. Move the brood chamber without the floor to one side, placing it diagonally on the upturned roof. You can now clean the floor or replace it with a new floor and then replace the brood chamber.

Clean the brood box

It is good practice to clean the brood box thoroughly in the early spring. If the weather is not suitable to expose the frames with brood and bees I may leave this until the first inspection in April. The easiest method is to move the brood box to one side and place another clean empty brood box on the clean floor. You can use the brood box from your reserve hive for swarm control. Simply place the frames into the clean box after your quick inspection. The used empty brood box can now be prepared ready to replace the brood box for the next hive.

The used box is scraped clean of bits of wax and propolis and scorched on the inside with a blow lamp. I smear a little petroleum jelly in the groove behind the runners and this helps to discourage the bees building up propolis between the frame lugs and brood box. This makes it easier to remove the frames from the brood box for the rest of the season.

Examine the combs

Remove the dummy board if fitted, checking that the queen is not on it, and place it against the front of the hive. This provides enough space for you to remove the next frame without 'rolling' the bees against the remaining frames. When you have examined the comb, you can replace it in the space the dummy board occupied.

Take out each comb in turn and examine each side, keeping the frame above the brood chamber so that if the queen falls off she will return to the brood nest. Look carefully at the brood, both sealed and open cells with eggs and larvae. Note how many frames have brood on them and estimate the equivalent full frames of food stores.

Place any old combs with mouldy pollen or patches of drone cells, which need changing, to the edge of the brood chamber. This will allow you to replace them with new combs next time you open the hive.

Remove and replace combs carefully so that you do not 'roll' or crush bees. There is no need to spend any time looking for the queen but if you do see her, replace the frame she is on carefully. A damaged queen at this stage could result in the colony dying out.

If you do not have a dummy board then you can place the first comb you take out against the front of the hive, so that the bees and queen, if you missed seeing her when you inspected the comb, can walk back into the hive through the entrance.

Combs with brood should not be left outside the hive as it may become chilled and die, especially in the early spring.

Is the colony queenright?

Look for patches of eggs and larvae and sealed cells without too many gaps, indicating a circular laying pattern. Only one egg in each cell and the cappings on sealed cells only slightly domed and regular are good signs that the queen is laying worker brood and the colony is queenright.

Monitoring varroa population

The autumn varroa treatment, together with the oxalic or lactic acid treatment you may have used in December, will have kept the varroa population down to a low level but a few mites will survive the winter on the adult bees. As brood-rearing increases, so does the opportunity for varroa to multiply.

To give your bees the best possible start in the spring and a clear run through the summer you need to make sure that the varroa population is kept at a low level. So early in March it is a good idea to monitor the varroa mite population by counting the number of mites that die naturally and planning the spring treatment if necessary. Insert the monitoring tray after you have cleaned or replaced the floor. Debris or dead bees on the floor will prevent some of the mites falling on to your monitoring tray.

Additional spring treatment is not needed if the average daily mite-drop is two or fewer. With more than two mites, you should consider some treatment to control the growth of the mite population. Several control methods are described in *Managing Varroa* and I suggest you discuss this with a local experienced beekeeper.

If the bees are dead

If you find that the bees are dead, make a note of what you find, do not clear away anything yet. As a precaution close the entrance to prevent other bees robbing any food and spreading disease. As soon as you can, ask for advice from an experienced beekeeper and try to establish the cause of death. Do not be discouraged but make a new start later in the year.

Lighting the smoker

There is usually an opportunity to make a quick inspection of the colony during a fine spell of weather this month. This will entail putting on a veil and any other protection you need so you will be able to concentrate on the colony and not worry about a sting! You also need to light the smoker. It's worth while practising lighting the smoker beforehand. Place a crumpled piece of burning newspaper in the bottom and get this well alight by slowly pumping the bellows. Then add the fuel while maintaining a good flow of air until the fuel is alight. The aim is to produce cool smoke and to keep the smoker going without too much attention.

Any available fuel may be used, such as wood shavings, dry rotten wood or pine cones, but most of these leave a sticky tarry deposit on the smoker and I have found that hessian sacking or cocoa shells sold at garden centres for mulching leave the smoker cleaner. To get cool smoke use a gentle pumping action of the bellows and add a little grass on top of the fuel.

The presence of willow bushes and trees in the neighbourhood is appreciated by beekeepers. They provide much needed nectar and yellow pollen early in the season

Nick Withers

Claire Waring

Willow flower

Jobs for March

- check food reserves and feed sugar syrup if needed
- carry out a quick inspection if the weather is suitable
- clean the hive floor or fit an open mesh floor
- monitor natural varroa mite drop and plan spring treatment if necessary
- prepare clean brood frames and foundation to replace comb in poor condition
- prepare supers with frames and foundation and a queen excluder
- prepare a spare hive with frames and foundation ready for swarm control
- study books or publications about managing varroa and honey bee diseases.

15 APRIL

April is the start of regular beekeeping activity when honey bee colonies change from simply surviving the winter months to developing into active mature colonies. They may go on to reproduce by swarming, replacing an ageing queen, and they gather enough food reserves to survive through the next winter.

In the process, with our help, they may produce surplus honey for us to gather. As always, the weather affects how quickly colonies develop and therefore how and when we act to help them.

COLONY ACTIVITY

The queen's egg-laying accelerates as the weather and available forage improves. If there is an early warm spring, you may see eggs in drone cells and later on the first drones will emerge, and early swarms may appear before the end of April. All the incoming nectar and pollen is used for colony maintenance. So from the beginning of April you need to check the colony to make sure that all is well and to look out for signs of swarming.

The brood population may be increasing faster than the adult population so if there is a sudden cold spell, there's a risk of brood starving and chilling as the population of adult bees may be too small to feed and cover the brood.

Apple blossom

The flowers of all fruit trees are valuable providers of nectar and pollen. Apple blossom is one of the best, producing a reddish yellow pollen. Honey bees are the most effective pollinators and are appreciated by fruit growers

Preparations for Swarming

A strong healthy colony may begin preparations for swarming. The first step is the construction of drone cells which at 6 mm across are slightly larger than worker cells. The queen lays unfertilised eggs in these cells. The egg hatches after three days and after another eight days the cell is sealed with a distinctive domed wax capping. The drone, the male bee, will emerge from the cell 24 days after the egg was laid. The drone is mature and ready to mate when it is about 14 days old.

Strong colonies will also produce a number of queen cell cups or play cups shaped like the cup part of an acorn. You may see eggs in a few of these play cups, another step in their preparations for issuing a swarm. Quite often the bees will not take the process beyond this stage and it is thought that the workers eat the eggs.

If the colony is intent on swarming the workers will allow the eggs in a few of the queen cups to hatch three days after they were laid and will immediately deposit a good supply of brood food or 'royal jelly' in the queen cups and begin to enlarge the cups to form queen cells. After another five days the cells are sealed with wax. Within a day or two, or more in poor weather, the old queen with about half the colony will swarm out of the hive.

The first virgin queen will finally emerge from the cell 16 days after the egg was laid or about seven or eight days after the first or 'prime' swarm left with the old queen. Her first job is to kill all her rival queens still in their cells. Quite often, depending on how many additional workers have emerged since the prime swarm left, the workers will defend the remaining queens in their cells and hassle the first virgin and send her out with a secondary swarm known as a 'cast'. This process can be repeated to the point when the mother colony is no longer viable.

HELPING THE COLONY

Regular inspections

April to June is probably the busiest time helping your bees to develop into productive colonies. This entails opening the hive regularly to examine and assess the condition of the colony. You need to check that it has adequate reserves of food, the bees have enough space, they are healthy with a laying queen and if they are preparing to swarm.

How often we carry out the inspection is determined by the timetable for swarming. A swarm usually leaves the hive after the first queen cell is sealed, which is eight days after the egg was laid. So if the egg was laid in the queen cell as soon as you closed up the hive after one of your regular inspections, the swarm will leave in another eight or nine days. Sometimes we may have to miss a day because of the weather or work and most of us live to a seven-day cycle, so the best plan is carry out a regular inspection every seven days. This will give a day's leeway for unforeseen circumstances or bad weather. When you open the hive you are aiming to answer the following questions:

1. Has the colony enough space?

First, are there plenty of empty cells near to the developing area of brood where the queen can lay more eggs? Sometimes you may find that the combs are still full of food. You should replace some of these with drawn comb, if available, or foundation. The combs you have removed should be stored in a bee-proof box or spare brood chamber. They will be useful for feeding a colony or nucleus hive later on.

Secondly, is there enough space for the bees to store incoming nectar? The queen excluder and first super should be put on when seven or eight frames in the brood chamber contain brood. More supers may be added as the bees cover 75% frames in the super.

Bees are sometimes reluctant to move through a queen excluder to enter a super full of foundation. It's a good idea to put on a super with foundation without the queen excluder in place. When the bees are in the super and starting to draw out the foundation then the queen excluder can be replaced. Make sure that the queen is in the brood box and not in the super. More than one super can be added at the same time in warm, settled weather.

2. Is the queen present and laying?

There is no need to try to find the queen. If you can see eggs then that is enough evidence that the queen was in the hive up to three days before. You can expect the egg-laying rate to increase week by week.

3a. Is the colony building up? (Early in the season)

You can measure colony growth by counting the number of frames containing brood every week and recording the result. If you have more than one colony you can compare their progress.

If you have only one colony find out how neighbouring beekeepers' colonies compare.

You will usually find that there is a wide variation in colony size when you compare the development of a number of colonies in an apiary or in a neighbourhood. In late April some will have seven or more frames with brood, most will have five or six and a few will be lagging behind.

If your colony is slower to develop than others in the neighbourhood it will be useful to try to find out the reason. It could be a poor queen or some other factor such as poor wintering conditions. Consult an experienced beekeeper so that you can take remedial action.

3b. Is the colony building queen cells? (later in the season)

Healthy colonies soon start building a number of potential queen cells called 'play cups' or 'queen cell cups'. These look like the cups that hold acorns with the opening pointing down. They are not significant while they are empty. There is no point in removing them as the bees will simply build more but it is important to check each one carefully.

If you find a play cup containing an egg without food this could mean that the bees are preparing to build queen cells but quite often they do not go on to the next stage. As a precaution, an egg without food should be destroyed because it could hatch as soon as you close the hive. The queen cell will then be developed and sealed in five days, so you would lose the swarm before your next inspection.

Make sure you have seen all the play cups. Some may be tucked into the edge between the comb and the side of the frame, or along the bottom of the frame.

If you keep your brood nest on a deep and a shallow box, known as a brood-and-a-half, you will usually find the play cups along the bottom of the frames in the top box. You can check for queen cells by simply tilting the top box and looking underneath.

A larva in a little pool of milky-looking brood food means that a daughter queen is being raised and swarm control action is needed. The cell will be sealed five days after the egg hatched. So if you find a larva and food in a play cup or an open queen cell you need to take swarm control action straight away. Finding a sealed queen cell means that the swarm and the queen have probably left!

4. Is there enough food until the next inspection?

You should always make sure at every inspection that the bees have a reserve of food of about 4 kg or the equivalent of two full National brood frames in case the weather turns cold or wet and the bees are unable to forage. The reserve will cover their needs until the next inspection. If they need food you can feed sugar syrup in a contact feeder or exchange a frame with food from another healthy colony.

5. Are there any signs of disease or abnormality?

I suggest that you first learn to recognise healthy brood and look out for and investigate anything abnormal. It may take some time to learn to recognise some diseases but we need to continue to persevere.

Keep a record of your assessment

It is difficult to remember afterwards what you found out during your examination so I would urge you to start keeping a record straight away even if you have only one hive. At first you could simply keep notes in an exercise book, or a card pinned inside the hive roof. In a year or two you may want to keep a few more colonies, then the record keeping and what you record becomes more important.

There is now a legal requirement to keep a record of any treatments introduced into the hive including the date. The colony record is probably the most convenient place to maintain this information.

I keep my colony record on an A5 sheet in a folder that I take with me to the apiary. The entry is made straight away after I have examined each colony. I take the record home so that I can check if I need any equipment to prepare or take with me to the 'out-apiary' for the next visit. The details of my record card is shown in Appendix 2.

Swarm control

As soon as you find occupied queen cells you should adopt your chosen method to manage the swarming procedure so that you don't lose half of your bees and probably all your honey crop for the year.

There are many different procedures you can use. If you have started using a particular method you have learned from an experienced beekeeper, persevere with it so that you become confident with one method before you try another. Don't try to follow bits of different methods. Once you have mastered one procedure and understand the principles then you can experiment if you wish.

Probably the most widely used method is known as the artificial swarm. This will maintain the maximum foraging force with the queen, who resumes egg-laying without interruption, which therefore minimises the loss of honey. If you follow the procedure carefully and do not miss seeing any queen cells it nearly always works. The detailed procedure is described in Chapter 6 on Swarming.

Comb replacement

Old comb can be a significant carrier of disease. It is good practice to replace brood comb by replacing the three or four oldest or most damaged combs with clean frames and foundation every year.

Some of the used combs with no damage or patches of drone cells may be reused after sterilising with acetic acid. The wax from the damaged comb can be recovered and the frames replaced or cleaned and fitted with foundation.

Save wax

Beeswax is a valuable product of the hive and it is worth while saving the small quantity that you may gather in your first year or two with one or two hives. You can collect bits of wax from brace and burr comb during your regular inspections from April to July. This wax should never be thrown away around the apiary as this can trigger robbing and spread disease. A suitable container with a lid for collecting the wax is a useful item in your tool box

You should wash the saved wax in soft water such as clean rain water and let it dry before storing it in a vermin proof box. Putting the box in the freezer for a day or two will kill any wax moth eggs. When you have saved enough you can clean and melt it into blocks and use it as you wish.

Prepare equipment to rescue a swarm

Rescuing a swarm is a very useful service we can provide to our community, who may be afraid of swarms. This is the time to gather some of the equipment you may need because you do not get much notice about a swarm that needs rescuing.

You will need a skep or strong cardboard box about the same size as a skep and a sheet of smooth porous material such as cotton, large enough to wrap around the box. Use glue or tape to fix the flaps forming the top of the box to the inside to create a smooth interior. This will prevent bees entering crevices and being squashed when the box is moved. Some other useful aids include secateurs and a long pole with a swarm-catching bag to reach swarms just out of reach from the ground.

Finding the queen

It is not necessary to find the queen during your regular inspections. However, as soon as you see occupied queen cells you need to find her. There are many other manipulations when the first instruction is to 'find the queen'. Many beginners, and even those who have kept bees for years, find it daunting and often give up without success.

The trouble is that it sounds difficult. You are trying to find one queen among forty thousand workers and hundreds of drones. The queen is different from all the other insects in the hive. She is taller, longer and walks in a different way. Think 'I can find the queen today'. As well as being mentally prepared, be prepared in a practical way too. What will you do when you find her? Will you place her in a cage or matchbox? Are your reading spectacles on if you need them?

The queen spends most of the time in the brood area where there are eggs. On a fine warm day, approach the hive quietly and use the minimum of smoke so that the bees and queen carry on with their work. Otherwise if you disturb the bees too much, they might run about all over the hive and the queen may move away from the brood nest to parts of the hive where you would not expect to find her.

Your handling should be gentle, firm and swift, not rough, hesitant or slow. Concentrate only on finding the queen. Do not be distracted by other work such as looking for eggs or checking play cups at the same time.

The horse chestnut produces masses of blossoms from late April or May, providing nectar and brick-red coloured pollen

A horse chestnut flower

Start at one end of the brood chamber and take out the dummy board or first frame and examine both sides carefully. You do not expect the queen to be on these but she is sometimes! Place the dummy board or first frame in a safe place to provide a space for the next frame in the brood chamber. I use a nuc box placed by the hive. Repeat with each frame until you reach frames with brood.

Hold the frame with brood over the hive, in case the bees and queen fall off, and look around the edge of the frame. The queen will usually move from the light into the dark and you may spot her moving to the other side of the frame. Or look at the frame as a whole and you may see her because she stands out from the pattern of workers.

Now focus in on small areas. Move your view in a circle around the frame from the edge to the centre. Pay particular attention to areas with eggs. Repeat the process on the other side and then on each frame.

As you remove each frame take a quick glance down the walls and on to the floor of the hive. Also look on the face of the comb you have just exposed.

Sometimes you can see her because she has longer legs and therefore is taller than the workers. The queen usually moves away from the light into a darker area, so as you remove each frame she may move to the other side of the next frame. If you did not find her first time you can repeat the process if the bees are still quiet. If they start running about all over the combs, it's probably better to try again later.

Another approach is to spread the frames in pairs using an extra brood chamber. Allow about 5 cm between each pair and the sides. The queen will move into the dark space between one of the pairs of frames. After about five minutes, take each pair in turn and open it like a book: you should find her quite easily.

Jobs to do in April

- start your regular inspections every week
- add a queen excluder and supers
- replace old comb with foundation or sterilised comb
- make sure your swarm control equipment is ready
- practise your chosen swarm control method before you find queen cells
- practise picking up and marking drones
- mark the queen and, if you wish, clip the queen's wing
- collect the equipment for rescuing swarms.

16 MAY

May is the month when everything is growing. The spring flowers are at their best, providing plenty of pollen and nectar for bees and, in a good season, providing surplus honey for beekeepers to gather around the end of the month. This is especially true if oilseed rape is grown in the vicinity.

May is a busy month for swarms and if your colony swarms you will lose your chance to gather much surplus honey. This is the time to stock your hive if this is your first year with bees.

COLONY ACTIVITY

As the weather warms up and there are ample sources of nectar and pollen for the foragers the colony expands rapidly. The queen fills the brood chamber with eggs and reaches her peak egg-laying rate later in the month. The expanding population of adult bees will need more space for themselves and to store and process nectar into honey.

Look out for signs of swarming preparations.

Recruiting more foragers

On a warm day you may catch sight of foragers recruiting more workers to join the foraging force. They do this inside the hive in the dark but sometimes you will see that they carry on with the dance on the comb as you remove it during one of your regular inspections. The foragers have found a good source of food and they indicate this to their sisters by passing on a little of the nectar to taste and at the same time perform a dance to indicate the location. The forager indicates the direction and distance from the hive by performing a figure of eight dance called a waggle or wagtail dance on the face of the comb. A round dance is a simpler message that the source is 'nearby', within about 100 metres from the hive.

Converting nectar into honey

The forager sucks up the nectar from the flowers and carries it back to the hive in her honey stomach or 'crop'. When she enters the hive she regurgitates the nectar and gives it to a house bee, who adds an enzyme and stores it initially in a warm part of the hive near the brood area, then in the supers. The house bees now reduce the moisture content of the nectar by hanging drops of nectar out to dry and creating a flow of air through the hive by standing still and 'fanning' their wings.

By the end of the month some of the honey stored in the supers will be 'ripe'; that means that the moisture content has been brought down to about 18%. The bees will cover the full cells with a layer of wax. Partly filled cells will not be covered even if the honey is ripe.

Bald brood and wax moth

You may see brood whose cappings have been removed without harming the pupae and they will eventually emerge as normal healthy bees. The culprit is a wax moth larva which hatched among the brood and chewed its way through the cappings. The wax moth larva covers the cells with a silky membrane that is removed by the bees to leave open cells with healthy pupae. The decapped cells are usually in a straight line with some cells still covered with the silk membrane.

HELPING THE COLONY

Wax moth

Strong healthy colonies usually do not suffer serious damage from wax moth. However, beekeepers usually kill the wax moth larvae. If you follow the surface of the straight line of cells covered with the silk membrane with the corner of your hive tool the wax moth larva usually appears at the end of the line.

Supering (adding supers)

It is a good plan to add more supers before the bees need more space. I suggest that when the bees are occupying 75% of the frames in the first super you put on in April, it is time to add another super. It does not matter if the super is not yet being used to store nectar. The increasing population of bees needs space to park themselves as well as to store nectar.

Nectar needs about three times the space to store it than the honey to which it will be converted. So this month be generous in adding supers well ahead of the bees' needs or else congestion in the brood chamber may trigger preparations for swarming.

When you add the second and subsequent supers with foundation it is a good idea to place a couple of frames with drawn comb from the first super on the outside against the walls of the super with the foundation in the middle to encourage the bees to go up into the super. Place it on the queen excluder underneath the first super you added. This is known as 'bottom' supering. It puts the foundation near to the brood chamber where the warmth helps wax production. Do not risk contaminating the honey with sugar syrup by feeding when nectar is being stored. If the additional super is full of drawn comb it does not seem to make any difference if it is added underneath or above the existing supers. Now it's up to the bees and the weather to make the most of the foraging opportunity in your area to fill the supers with honey.

Stocking your hive

If you do not yet have bees, this is a good time to stock your hive. You can start with a nucleus and develop your confidence as the little colony grows. Or you can start with a swarm, available free for you to collect, so make sure you tell your local beekeeping group that you would like to hear about any available swarms. Most groups have appointed swarm coordinators to let beekeepers know about reported swarms.

Starting with a nucleus

You may be able to buy a nucleus from a local supplier or from the equipment suppliers. They are usually on five frames with at least three frames of brood. They are delivered, or if from a local supplier, may be collected by you, in a well ventilated nucleus hive.

As soon as it arrives, place the nucleus on the hive stand you have prepared for your full size hive, the entrance in the same position as the hive entrance will be. Open the entrance to let the bees fly out to explore and orientate themselves to their new location. You can now cover the top ventilation screen to shut out the light and rain if expected, so that the bees will orientate on the position of the entrance. Leave the little colony to settle for a couple of hours or overnight.

Transfer the frames to your own hive as follows. Move the nucleus hive to one side, place your full size hive on the stand and transfer the frames one at a time, maintaining the relative position of all the frames because there may be variation in the thickness of parts of the combs. The five frames from the nucleus should occupy the centre of the brood chamber. Fill the space with foundation on both sides.

You will help the nucleus to grow by feeding with sugar syrup until all the foundation is fully drawn out.

There is a good chance that a nucleus transferred to a full hive this month will develop in time to provide a small honey crop by the end of July. A later nucleus will develop during the summer and be strong enough to prepare for winter in the autumn.

Starting with a swarm

A description of how to collect and hive a swarm is given in Chapter 6. It can be quite straightforward if the swarm is hanging from a branch about one or two metres from the ground. The main challenge is that swarms sometimes settle in awkward places. Some swarms will be difficult to rescue and some impossible. If you are apprehensive about attempting this on your own, ask for advice from the swarm coordinator or experienced beekeeper in your local group. Perhaps you will be able to watch a beekeeper collecting a swarm or you may get help with your first one.

You may be presented with a swarm in a skep or cardboard box already collected by a beekeeper and ready to be 'hived'. There is guidance in Chapter 6 on how to proceed and look after the hived swarm.

MOVING COLONIES

As soon as bees fly out from a hive or nuc for the first time they fly around in circles for a while to orientate to their new location by sight and remembering landmarks such as hives and bushes. Next time they fly out they will return to the exact position of the hive entrance. If the hive is moved the homecoming bees may enter another nearby hive or be lost. So if you want to move the hive sideways within the apiary you can do it by moving the hive in steps of up to about a metre at a time. If you are moving the hive backwards across an open space you can move it about two metres at a time. You should allow a day or two of flying weather between each step to give the bees time to settle to the new position

During the winter when bees have been confined to the hive for a week or two they may be moved gently to another part of the apiary in one step.

If bees are moved beyond their flight range of about three miles they will re-orient to the new location. There are a number of precautions necessary to protect the bees. One of the main dangers during the journey is suffocation due to overheating.

Hive with bees ready to move. Note the two straps side by side for extra security during the journey. A travelling screen is not needed if you have an open mesh floor. Make sure there is plenty of space underneath the floor to allow the air to circulate to avoid overheating in the hive

- if you are using a solid floor with your hive you should replace the crownboard with ventilation screen otherwise the bees will become overheated and suffocate. Hives with open mesh floors will be sufficiently ventilated but make sure that there is a gap under the floor to allow plenty of air to enter the hive during the journey
- use two hive straps in parallel to securely fasten together the floor, brood box, supers and screen or crownboard with the feed hole closed
- after the bees have stopped flying, close the entrance to keep them in the hive

- move the bees during the cool of the evening or early morning if you can. Spray with water if the bees become agitated during a long journey or during an unavoidable stop
- as soon as you arrive at your destination place the hive on the prepared site without delay. If you have used a ventilation screen place the crownboard on top and replace the roof. Open the entrance and retreat promptly because the bees may be quite agitated
- remove the ventilation screen and straps after the bees have settled during your next visit.

Spring honey with oilseed rape (OSR)

Your bees will enjoy working on some crops of oilseed rape (OSR) and it can provide a good crop of spring honey. Some hybrid varieties, however, are not so attractive to bees so you cannot be sure that the sight of the bright yellow flowers in fields near your apiary will give a good flow of nectar.

The flavour is mild, and pure OSR honey is white, very similar in appearance to lard. It often granulates with very fine crystals which are very smooth on the tongue. In this case it's very useful as a 'seed' for blending with other honey to produce a light golden smooth honey that is a favourite with many customers.

The abundance of nectar and pollen from OSR stimulates the rapid development of colonies. The eggs laid during this time will provide the additional foraging force just in time for the main summer flow usually starting at the end of June or early July. Colonies working the OSR will draw out foundation without the need for feeding with sugar syrup.

There are some beekeepers that are less than enthusiastic about OSR. The honey crystallises very quickly so if the supers are full of OSR honey and the bees leave it to cool or the weather turns cold, the honey may set in the comb making it difficult to extract. Therefore, to gather the crop before it crystallises you will need to keep a careful watch on the weather, the OSR honey in the hive and the crop in the fields. Other plants that produce nectar which will crystallise quickly include mustard and kale.

When you see the OSR fields in flower, keep an eye on the frames in the supers. When some cells are being capped you can test to see if the honey is ripe by holding the frame horizontally above the open hive, to avoid spilling nectar on the ground, and giving it a single shake to see if any nectar comes out. If it does not drop out the nectar has been changed to honey and is ready to extract. You may find that some of the middle frames in one or two supers are ripe, that is ready to be extracted, so you could move all the frames with ripe honey into one super and take it for harvesting the same day.

Keep an eye on the fields of OSR and when they are 80% green, be ready to take off all the OSR honey straight away. Don't use bee escapes or clearer boards to separate the bees from the supers as this will take a couple of days and will allow the OSR to cool and crystallise. I suggest that you take each frame, shake and brush the bees off, then take them for extracting the same day. Return the empties as soon as you can. If you find some combs with nectar not ready to extract, gather them in one super and keep it on the hive a few more days.

It is best to remove all the OSR honey, as any that is left may make your summer honey also difficult to extract. However, be very careful to make sure that your bees have plenty of food reserves as you remove the OSR crop. There may be a shortage of nectar in many areas as the spring flowers fade and perhaps the summer flowers are not yet ready. This is known as the 'June gap'. If you find there are no food reserves in the brood chamber I suggest you leave three or four frames of OSR honey in the super and remove them as soon as you see nectar being stored in the supers. Sometimes there is no gap if spring is late or summer is early or if you have June flowering forage nearby.

Nick Withers

Oilseed rape is a good source of nectar and pollen and bees returning from a foraging trip often have a tell tale mark of the yellow pollen on their heads

Nick Withers

Hawthorn flowers

Hawthorn produces a spectacular array of flowers but the nectar flow is unpredictable. When the flow occurs the high quality honey is dark amber colour and the pollen olive green

Jobs to do in May

- if you have not already done an artificial swarm, carry on with the seven-day inspections looking out for open queen cells with larvae and food and immediately take swarm control action
- be generous with supers, adding another before it is needed by the bees
- keep an eye on any OSR crops in your area, remove 'ripe' honey in supers and remove it all when the OSR fields turn green if there are food reserves in the brood box
- be prepared to collect swarms or do an artificial swarm at short notice by keeping equipment and a hive with frames of foundation ready
- arrange to take delivery of a nucleus if this is how you intend to start beekeeping
- reserve a honey extractor from your beekeeping association, if available, ready for your spring crop.

17 JUNE

If you started out with bees last year, then June may be the month when you will harvest your first crop of honey. If you are new to beekeeping this year, you have probably just started with your first 'nuc' or swarm and will be keeping your fingers crossed for some honey in late July or early August.

COLONY ACTIVITY

Where there is a June gap there is quite suddenly little or no forage for a large force of bees that may have just experienced the bumper spring flow. Do not be surprised if the bees are a bit more defensive than during the early spring.

The queen's egg-laying rate peaked in late May or early June and the population of adult bees will be at its maximum 21 days later, near the end of June or early July, just in time for the main nectar flow from the summer flowers.

June is one of the main months for swarming so look out for the preparations in the hive.

May and June is the peak time for swarms. This swarm was rescued by brushing it into a box placed on its side on the ground near the swarm

Comb building

You may see wax-making bees clustering to provide the warmth needed to draw out the cells on the beeswax foundation you presented to a rescued swarm or added to a nucleus. They mainly use the wax of the foundation. The bees secrete little white wax cakes from four pairs of wax glands underneath the abdomen, but they add very little extra wax to the cells for rearing brood. They add more wax to the slightly deeper cells for storing food because they need only allow space between combs to accommodate one bee at a time to fill the cells. The space between adjacent cells used for brood-rearing is larger to accommodate bees working simultaneously back to back.

A small colony with a young queen will usually build only worker cells. A colony in the second year with an older queen will build drone cells as well as worker cells. Drone cells may be built along the bottom edge of the frames and the bees often tear down patches of worker cells to make room for them.

HELPING THE COLONY AND HARVESTING

Regular inspections

Continue the regular weekly inspections. This is one of the main swarming months when quite suddenly there may be little forage from the spring flowers.

Varroa control

Monitor the varroa mite population by counting the number of mites that die naturally or by examining drone pupae. Plan the autumn treatment and buy the supplies as needed.

Extracting spring honey

I have always found extracting the spring crop of honey a bit more tricky than the main summer crop. OSR honey will crystallise very quickly as it cools so it is best to move supers containing spring honey with OSR to your extracting room without delay. The supers should be covered to prevent bees reclaiming the honey. Also try to keep the supers warm as you take them from the apiary to the extractor. Do the extracting in a warm room as soon as possible after bringing the supers in from the apiary.

The most suitable room in most homes will be the kitchen. I suggest that you prepare the kitchen by clearing everything away from the work surfaces and the floor and covering them with newspaper. This will absorb any spilled honey, and the newspaper can all be gathered up afterwards. Ideally you should take the supers of honey off the hives, extract the honey and replace the supers and wet frames on the hive straight away and on the same day.

Decapping using a knife. The piece of wood is fitted with nails to prevent it slipping across the top of the pan. The nail in the centre supports the frame. The frame is sloped forward so that the sheet of cappings falls away from the comb face as it is cut. The steel vacuum flask of hot water is to clean and heat the fluted decapping knife; it is dried with a cloth before the next cut. This works well with frames evenly filled with capped comb

Geoff Close

Decapping using a decapping fork. The frame is placed on the dish to collect the honey that will fall out and the fork is used to remove the cappings. The fork does not need to be heated or washed between cuts and works well with even and uneven combs. It takes a little more time. Take care to keep your hands and fingers behind the frame away from the danger of the knife or fork slipping

Geoff Close

Even if you have been careful and taken the frames off before they have crystallised, you may still find some patches of set honey in some of the combs. You will see the crystallised honey as you use a decapping knife or fork to remove the wax cappings.

I find that the best way to deal with these combs is to scrape the patches of honey and wax down to the midrib into a container. This mixture of wax and crystallised honey is placed in a warming cabinet at around 40°C until the honey has liquefied. The wax will float on the honey and both may be recovered.

Do remember to keep all the wax cappings in another clean container. The honey can be washed off these with soft water and can be used to make mead. The cappings can be melted to make prize-winning blocks of wax or exchanged for foundation.

Using the extractor

This is probably the most expensive single item of beekeeping kit you may want to buy. At first I suggest you try to borrow one from your beekeeping group. Using one will help you to decide if you want to invest in a tangential extractor, suitable for a beekeeper with two or three hives, or a radial extractor that will suit a beekeeper with more hives or planning to expand.

Always remember to place frames of about the same weight on opposite sides of the extractor cage to balance the load.

Take care not to spin the cage too quickly with frames full of honey particularly with a tangential extractor. At first you should spin the frames slowly to remove some of the honey from the cells on the outside of the frames. Then turn the frames so that the other side with full cells is on the outside and spin slowly again before increasing the spin speed to remove more honey. Now turn the frames again to do a fast spin on the first side.

You do not have to remove, turn and replace the frames in a radial extractor but it's still a good idea to increase the spin speed slowly. You can easily end up with the comb collapsing, resulting in a mixture of wax and honey in the bottom of the extractor and the loss of a good comb. New comb needs special care to prevent this happening.

Settling

The best way to deal with a small quantity for consumption by friends and family is to run the honey from the extractor straight into a container and allow it to settle for a day in a warm room. Most of the debris such as bits of wax will either float or sink. You can skim off the top and carefully transfer the clean honey into jars, taking care not to disturb the debris at the bottom of the container.

The honey in the jars will quite quickly cloud as it begins to crystallise. If you want clear honey simply warm the jars of honey in a water bath at about 55°C for up to 45 minutes.

Straining

Spring honey containing any OSR is very difficult to strain unless the honey is warmed. Honey from the extractor collected in buckets may be warmed in an insulated box to around 40°C to clear the crystals so that it will run through strainers or a straining cloth.

You should store the honey in food-grade containers with air-tight lids in a cool dry place.

Bottling

Do remember that honey is a food, subject to food hygiene regulations, so from the hive to the jar, keep it covered in clean conditions all the time. Use only food-grade stainless steel or polythene utensils and containers. Avoid placing supers of honey on the ground. Honey absorbs moisture and is easily spoilt by overheating. If you are planning to sell honey make sure that you fully understand and follow the legal requirements for its labelling and sale.

Emergency summer feeding

If the weather deteriorates suddenly after you have removed the honey crop in mid season, a strong colony can quickly use up all the food reserves in the brood box. If you feed sugar syrup there is a risk the bees will store it in the empty supers where it will contaminate the next crop of honey. There are other ways to provide emergency food with the supers on the hive waiting for the next nectar flow.

One way is to return some frames of honey to the empty supers if they are still available. Another way is to replace one of the empty brood frames with a frame of stores you removed in April when you were making room for the queen to lay. If you do not have any frames with food in them available you can make up a brood frame of emergency store of sugar. Take an empty brood frame, place it horizontally and sprinkle sugar to fill the cells, then dampen the sugar with a spray of water. After a little while you can repeat the process to fill the cells on the other side. The bees will take the sugar when they need it and ignore it when they can get nectar outside.

Jobs to do in June

- remove the spring honey from the hive and extract straight away
- keep a careful watch for food shortage after removing the honey
- feed if necessary but avoid sugar syrup being stored in the supers
- carry on with weekly inspections and take swarm control action if needed
- carry on collecting swarms
- monitor for varroa and plan and buy treatment as needed.

Sometimes bees cheat the broad beans by collecting nectar through a hole at the base of the flower cut by short-tongued bumble bees. Honey bees go in through the front of the flower to gather dark olive coloured pollen. Nectar can also be collected from the dark spots on the underside of the leaf bases, the stipules. These 'extra-floral nectaries' secrete nectar in sunny weather

18 JULY

July is the time for the main nectar flow. The bees collect more food than they need for maintenance and start to build up their stores of food for winter.

You have cared for the colony throughout the season. You have provided a good habitat in a good location, and protected them from predators and disease. You have provided room for them to expand at the right time and enabled them to reproduce without the loss of the mother colony. This month you will be rewarded with part of the golden harvest.

COLONY ACTIVITY

The queen's egg-laying rate peaked in early June and 21 days later the adult bee population will be at its highest. The peak population is just in time for the main nectar flow. The egg-laying will continue to fall during July so there will be an increasing proportion of adult bees that are foragers as fewer bees are needed for nursing larvae. Less food is required for colony maintenance so more is available to add to the supers.

Most colonies build queen cells during periods of little nectar flow in May and June. There seems to be less inclination to swarm during the main nectar flow. The precise timing will depend on the locality and, of course, the weather.

HELPING THE COLONY AND HARVESTING

Robbers

If you use a large entrance this should be reduced as the flow of nectar dries up, to reduce the risk of robbing by bees from other colonies and to prevent wasps entering the hive.

Supering

When the nectar flow starts, things get very busy for the foragers. Beekeepers need to continue with regular inspections and keep an eye on the supers. Some go away on holiday during the nectar flow but I do not recommend it. I did go abroad on business for three weeks during the flow when I looked after some WBC hives. It turned out to be a wonderful summer and on my return I found all the supers full and wild comb and honey packing the space between the lifts and brood box and supers.

As soon as the main nectar flow starts most colonies seem to forget about swarming. However, there is still a small risk of swarm preparations being started, particularly if the bees do not have enough room to store nectar.

A glance in the top super is enough to tell you when another is needed. Always add another super ahead of the bees' need for more space. When the bees are covering most of the frames you should add another super.

Do remember that for storing and processing nectar they use about three times the space that is needed to store the honey.

Keeping an eye on the need for supers during the flow will help you to avoid under- and also over-supering. Too many supers may result in all being partially filled, making more work for you when removing them to extract the honey crop.

It's a good idea to stop adding supers a week or two before the flow stops. This will encourage the bees to store some food in the brood chamber, which will provide food for the bees when you take off the supers.

It is not easy to know when the flow will end. I suggest you ask your local experienced beekeepers what they do because when the main nectar flow finishes depends on the local forage and the weather.

How do you know if the main nectar flow has started? Of course you can find out by asking local beekeepers. You can also tell by the purposeful activity in the apiary. The bees are leaving the hive entrance apparently quite clear in which direction they want to go and returning to deposit their load of nectar to the receiving house bees.

The scent of nectar processing in the apiary is another signal. During one of your inspections in late June or early July you will be pleased to discover heavier supers after what seemed a very long period when very little progress was evident.

Is the honey ready?

The main nectar flow will be over any time from mid to late July in the south and later in the north. Removing the surplus honey as soon as it is ready will give you time to complete any necessary varroa treatment and prepare the colony for winter from mid August at the latest.

It is important that the honey is 'ripe' before you take off the supers. 'Ripe' means that the water content is about 18%. Honey stored with the water content more than this is likely to spoil by fermentation. The figure for heather honey is a little higher.

The water content can be measured by using a refractometer but you do not need to do this to check your honey. The bees know when the honey is ripe. If the cells containing the honey are capped you can be sure that the honey is ready.

A few of the cells may not be capped and you can check if the honey in these is ready if you hold the frame horizontally and give it a sharp shake downwards. If some of the 'honey' falls out it is not ready. Its water content is too high. Frames containing honey that is not ready should be left for a few more days to let the bees finish the processing. The bees do not cap partly filled cells even if the honey is ready. They are waiting for more nectar to come in!

The bees fill the supers, process the honey and cap the cells working from the middle of the supers. The frames on the outside of the supers may have a higher proportion of uncapped cells than those at the centre. You can gather the frames on the outside of all the supers into one super for the bees to finish capping.

Clearing the supers

The calmest and gentlest way to move the bees from the supers is to use a clearer board. This is a board placed underneath the super to be cleared. It allows the bees to move from the supers into the brood chamber or another super below the board.

The traditional clearer board is made by fitting one or two Porter bee escapes in a crownboard. You will still need another crownboard to cover the supers. When the bees have moved from the super through the Porter bee escape to the box below they are unable to return through the one-way valve. This system works well provided the escape is clean when you install it in the crownboard. The little springs can sometimes be propolised if they are left on the hive after you have finished clearing the supers.

Sometimes stray drones will get stuck and block the escape route. It is easily cleaned using warm water with washing soda. The metal springs should be set to allow a gap of about 2 mm for the bees to pass through. As you will need to buy a second crownboard to use as a clearer board you could get one with two holes to accommodate two Porter bee escapes to reduce the risk of a complete blockage.

Clearer board. This is simply a crownboard fitted with Porter bee escapes

Other types of clearer boards have no moving parts, for example, the Canadian type. Instead they make the bees leave the supers through a hole and then through a passage or tunnel to exit into the box below some distance away from the access to the tunnel. The bees seem to learn the way back to the supers if they are left on for more than two days.

All the different types of escape work well in good flying weather. The traditional Porter bee escape works better than other types if the bees are slow to clear because of poor weather. It is best to allow two days of fine weather for most of the bees to move through the clearer board to the box below.

If the weather turns cold or wet, most of the bees stay put in the supers! Make sure there is space for the bees below the clearer board. An empty super beneath the clearer board will give the bees plenty of room especially if you are clearing two or three supers at once. It is best not to try to clear more than three supers in one go. Check carefully that there are no gaps or any way into the supers for bees or wasps to enter. The supers can be robbed out very quickly without any bees to defend the precious crop.

You may still find a few bees hanging around in the super even after two fine days with the clearer board on. If you want to make sure that there are no bees at all when you take the super into the extracting room, the stragglers will have to be brushed off each frame.

Shake and brush

If your bees are foraging on the summer flowers of spring-sown OSR or related crops such as mustard and kale that crystallise quickly, the clearer board should not be used. Some of the honey may crystallise in the comb during the two days for clearing when the bees have vacated the supers. A quick way to move the bees from the supers is simply to shake and brush the bees from each frame.

You will need a spare empty super placed on an upturned hive roof or in a wheelbarrow. Take each frame in turn and give it a couple of sharp downward shakes to remove most of the bees. The few remaining bees are brushed off with a bee brush or feather.

Each frame is placed in the empty super and covered with a cloth straight away to keep it clear of the many bees flying around. You should now quickly remove the full super without bees to a bee-proof place.

Repeat the process with the now empty super on the hive used to take the cleared frames from the next super. There is inevitably a bit of excitement going on while you are shaking and brushing the bees from 30 or more frames. It is much easier to work in pairs to get the shaking and brushing done smoothly and quickly. Try to arrange to work with another neighbouring beekeeper who will probably have honey from the same forage as yours.

I use the shake and brush method very early on a cool morning because the disturbed flying bees quickly return to the comfort of the hive. Then I have time to do the extracting and return the empty supers to the hives in the evening for the bees to take the remnants of honey from the combs.

Chemical repellents

If your bees are near to neighbours you may be tempted to use chemical repellents to move bees from supers containing honey that may crystallise quickly. It is claimed that the bees move quickly from the supers without any fuss.

I have no experience of using the repellents that are now available and I do not know what chemicals are used. However, I do not recommend using them to clear bees from supers. My view is that we need to avoid spraying chemicals or creating fumes in supers full of honey as there is a risk of contaminating the honey. We must take care to protect and maintain its reputation as a natural pure food with medicinal properties and no added preservatives or other contaminants.

Instead, I suggest that you talk to your neighbours and explain what you need to do to remove the supers quickly. Most people, I'm sure, will be sympathetic and will be happy to accommodate the excitement of the shake and brush procedure. After all, it will only happen once or twice a year, and a jar of honey is a good sweetener! If you do the job very early in the morning your neighbours are probably not yet up and about.

Leave some honey for the bees

The honey we take is that which is surplus to the bees' needs. Make sure that you do not take all their food reserves away. The bees may have started filling the brood box with nectar as the queen continues to lay fewer eggs, making more space available for food stores.

Sometimes the bees have stored all their incoming food in the supers and not stored any food in the brood chamber. Make sure there is food left for the bees. In most areas there will be more foraging opportunities in the autumn, sometimes after a gap in August.

After you have taken off the surplus honey for yourself, why not give the bees a gallon of sugar syrup anyway? Not only will the bees enjoy a little comfort after losing some of their hard-earned crop, but this incoming food may stimulate egg-laying. Sometimes in August the queen goes off laying for a short while. A little boost in egg-laying now will help increase the population of young bees for winter.

The summer harvest

Extracting the main summer honey harvest is usually easier than extracting the spring honey. This is because the summer crop is taken as soon as the honey is ready in late July or early August and rarely contains honey that crystallises quickly, so there is no need to scrape combs down to the midrib to remove solid honey and wax.

The honey flows well and will pass through a very fine straining bag or cloth without additional warming. It is still a good idea to extract the honey in a warm room and as soon as you can after removing the supers from the hive.

Washing up

As soon as you have finished extracting and bottling the honey you should do the washing-up. First of all the extractor and all the utensils used should be rinsed well in cold water. If you use hot water the bits of wax will melt and be smeared all over the utensils. Cold water rinsing will remove the beeswax, which can be recovered.

After the cold rinsing you can use hot water and when everything is clean and dry the equipment can be put away ready for the next harvest.

What to do with the empty supers

The supers with the wet frames can be returned to the hives for the bees to clear the remnants of honey from the combs. The bees do an excellent job of cleaning off all the honey leaving the frames dry and clean to handle. The best time to place the supers back on the hive is at the end of the day to reduce the risk of excitement, which can lead to robbing.

The supers should be placed on the hive they came from, above the crownboard with the feed hole partially covered to allow a small passage for the bees to move into the supers. This will encourage the bees to take the honey into the brood nest or to the super you have left on the hive. Sometimes they will simply gather the honey into a frame in the centre of the super above the crownboard instead of to their permanent quarters. If this happens you could try making a bigger gap between the brood area and frames to be cleared, by placing an empty super above the crownboard.

You can place the wet wax cappings in a dish above the crownboard in the same way as the wet supers. After a couple of days the bees will have taken the honey and the cappings will be clean and dry.

Nick Withers

Honey bee on a blackberry flower

Jobs to do in July

- add supers ahead of the bees' needs and avoid under- and over-supering
- reduce entrances, to avoid risk of robbing by bees and wasps
- reserve the extractor if you intend to hire it from your local association
- collect the utensils needed to transfer the honey from the super to the jar
- remove the surplus honey when it is ready.

The wild blackberry is one of the most common plants to be found in the country and is very attractive to bees. It commences flowering in June or July, producing nectar and grey-coloured pollen. The flowering period extends over several weeks with buds, flowers and fruit in all stages present at the same time

19 HIVE PRODUCTS

HONEY

With one hive and perhaps starting with a swarm or nucleus at the end of May, the harvest may be 5 to 20 kg depending on the summer weather. This quantity can be transferred straight into honey jars and given away as gifts to friends and neighbours and all may be consumed within a few weeks.

If you are in your second year with two or three hives and more skill in beekeeping, your honey harvest could be anything up to 60 kg in a good summer. I remember in my second year running my entire harvest into about 120 jars and after about six weeks having to liquefy about 100 jars of unattractive-looking crystallised honey, so that I could start again.

Clear honey in jars gradually changes its appearance as the honey begins to granulate. The appearance of the honey in jars as it changes from clear liquid to set crystallised honey is not attractive. Crystallised honey sometimes develops a frosted appearance on the sides of the jar if it is stored where the temperature fluctuates. This is not as attractive as the beautiful golden honey when it was first run into the jars. Of course, the honey is still fine and good to eat but some people think that it is spoilt. You can avoid this by storing the honey in bulk and producing only enough honey in jars to last for a month or so.

Honey from some flowers crystallises or sets in such a way as to give a gritty feel in the mouth when eaten. Other honeys, such as from oilseed rape (OSR), crystallise with a fine grain producing a very smooth feel on the tongue. I believe that most people prefer a smooth texture and you can quite easily produce all your soft-set honey with a smooth texture if you wish. Another characteristic of honey is that the first time it granulates it can become rock hard. When honey is granulated for the second time it will keep the soft-set texture longer.

You can store honey in 15 kg food-grade plastic buckets with air-tight lids and keep it in a cool place. This will crystallise within a few weeks, the time taken depending on the source of nectar.

Here is how I produce clear and soft-set honey starting with a 15 kg bucket of granulated honey. I strain my honey through a 200 micron bag when it is taken from the extractor, before it is run into the settling tank and then the storage bucket.

Jars of soft-set and clear honey, some to eat, some to give to friends and some to sell

Clear honey

- warm the bucket at no more than 50°C for one to two days until the honey is completely liquid
- pour the liquid honey into a settling tank. Use a strainer if this was not done when extracting
- keep the settling tank in a warm room for about one day to allow the air bubbles to rise to the surface
- skim off the surface air bubbles
- run the honey into clean warm dry jars. Place the lids on straight away.

I find that this clear honey will stay looking good in the jar for more than a month. If you are intending to enter your honey for competitions, or for extra clarity, warm the jars after bottling, in a water bath at 62°C for no more than one hour.

Soft-set honey

Some naturally granulated honey becomes very hard and gritty. By adding about 5% of a honey having a smooth texture you can produce a soft-set honey with a consistent smooth texture. This procedure is called 'seeding' the honey.

- warm the bucket at no more than 50°C for one to two days until the honey is completely liquid
- pour the liquid honey into a settling tank. Use a strainer if this was not done when extracting
- prepare the smooth-textured seed such as OSR honey, by warming 1 to 1.5 kg of this until it is the same consistency as porridge. Keep the temperature below 30°C to make sure that the crystals do not melt
- allow the liquid honey to cool to below 30°C and then add the seed honey. Mix thoroughly but avoid adding air
- allow to settle for a day or two
- skim off the air bubbles
- run the honey into clean dry jars. Place the lids on straight away
- keep 2 to 3 kg aside as the seed for the next batch
- store the jars in a cool place, ideally 14°C, until the honey is set.

The honey will set in three or four days at a temperature of about 14°C. It will take longer at higher or lower temperatures.

Do remember that honey is a food product and must be processed and handled with the highest standards of care and hygiene. There is a lot of legislation that covers the preparation of honey and it applies even if you only want to give honey away as gifts. Make sure that you understand what the legislation means for processing honey and if necessary ask for advice from your Environmental Health Officer at your local authority.

MEAD

Mead is a wine made with honey and may be the first alcoholic drink used by mankind. You can make a dry or sweet mead and experiment with adding various spices to make metheglin.

If you are an amateur wine maker you will already have some of the equipment needed to make mead. I have made mead and it is pleasant to drink especially at a gathering of beekeepers. Many friends who are not beekeepers are usually quite interested too. Dry mead may be ready to drink after about two or three years and sweet mead after four or five years.

Here is a basic recipe and method that I use which is based on a description in the book *Mead Making, Exhibiting and Judging* by Dr Harry Riches.

Mead – probably the first alcoholic drink
used by mankind

Ingredients:

    1.4 kg light honey
    3.4 litres water
    1 teaspoon yeast nutrient
    2 tablespoons cold strong tea
    Juice of 1 lemon
    1 tablet of vitamin B1
    Campden tablets
    Sugar, water, lemon juice and Marmite for the starter bottle.

Method:

- prepare the activated yeast by placing 140 ml water in a sterilised starter bottle, add a teaspoon of sugar, a teaspoon of lemon juice and a ¼ teaspoon of Marmite and mix well. Add a dry wine yeast such as Chablis, place a bung of cotton wool in the neck and stand the bottle in a warm airing cupboard for 48 hours. Bubbles will appear around the surface indicating the yeast is alive and ready to use
- prepare the must by mixing the honey and water in a sterilised bucket or fermentation bin. Aim for a specific gravity, measured with a hydrometer, of 1.080. Add the yeast nutrient, lemon juice, tannin, crushed B1 tablet and one crushed Campden tablet, stir, cover with a cloth and keep in a warm place for 48 hours
- after 48 hours, stir the must vigorously to get rid of the sulphur dioxide and introduce oxygen. Add the activated yeast in the starter bottle. Keep the covered bucket in a warm place for a day or two until fermentation starts, indicated by some froth on the surface
- leave the must to ferment for about 24 hours then pour it into a clean sterilised demijohn, filling it to about 5 cm from the top, to allow space for vigorous fermentation. Fit an air lock and place the demijohn in a cool dark place at around 15°C. When the fermentation has settled, top up the demijohn with cold boiled water to about 2 cm of the bung holding the air lock
- when fermentation has finished after four to six weeks, indicated by the absence of bubbles escaping through the air lock, the clear mead should be siphoned (racked) off the deposit (the lees) in the bottom of the demijohn, into a clean sterilised container. The demijohn should be washed clean and refilled with the mead and one crushed Campden tablet added, and topped up with cold boiled water. Replace the air lock. The specific gravity should be near 1.000, perhaps as low as 0.995
- store the demijohn in a cool dark place and after two or three weeks rack the mead again. Repeat the racking process every few weeks until the mead is clear and fermentation has finished. Replace the air lock with a cork and after a year the mead should be clear and bright and can be bottled. It should be ready to drink after a few more months.

BEESWAX

Beeswax is a valuable product of the hive and it is worth while saving the small quantity that you may gather in your first year or two with one or two hives. You can collect bits of wax from brace and burr comb during your regular inspections from April to July.

Cappings wax is the choice wax for making wax blocks for entering competitions. If you do not want to enter competitions, wax blocks can be exchanged for foundation or part exchanged for equipment. Or you can expand your product range by making beeswax polish, cosmetics and candles, if that takes your fancy!

You can expect to gather up to 800 g of wax per colony each year during the season, though it will probably be less in your first year. It is surprising how much debris you find when wax is melted, even from washed cappings which appear so clean.

Cleaning beeswax

You need to be very careful when you are melting beeswax. It is very combustible and an open flame must never be used to heat a container of water and beeswax. The mixture can suddenly foam and spill over the rim of the container and the spilled wax can easily ignite, producing a fierce fire. I know of one instance of a kitchen fire started in this way which needed attendance by a fire engine and a complete redecoration!

For small quantities of wax you gather in your first two or three years of beekeeping, a porringer or double saucepan will work well. Place the cappings or bits of wax to be cleaned in clean soft water such as rain water in the inside saucepan. Most double saucepans have a rim on the inside pan, so your mixture of water and wax should not be above this rim or you will be unable to remove the cake of wax.

As soon as the wax begins to melt, turn down the heat to maintain the temperature. You should avoid boiling the mixture. When all the wax is melted, let it all cool slowly so that the larger bits of debris sink to the bottom of the pan. When the cake of wax is cooled it will contract and can be removed from the pan.

The rim on the double saucepan means that only small amounts of wax can be processed in one go. Some books suggest pouring melted wax through a nylon filter but I have not succeeded using this method. The filter clogs up with solid wax as soon as I start pouring. So here is another method for cleaning wax using kitchen utensils, which filters the wax at the same time.

Place a clean empty basin inside a steamer, and the washed wax wrapped in a muslin bag or something similar in the top pan. Bring the water in the steamer up to the boil and keep it gently simmering. The steam in the top pan melts the wax which drips into the basin together with a small amount of condensate. Some of the condensate runs down the inside of the bottom pan into the simmering water. Be careful not to allow the steamer to run dry.

You can remove the bag when it has been reduced to a soggy lump in the bottom of the top pan. When cool, the wax cake formed on the condensate in the basin can be removed. My steamer will hold about 700 g of bits of wax and brace comb in half of the leg of a pair of tights. After about one hour on a gentle simmer, a 320 g cake of beeswax is produced.

Steamer. The basin of wax is raised on a wooden support to allow a greater volume of water for simmering

The beeswax harvest can be around 800 g per colony in a year

Solar wax extractor

A solar wax extractor is a useful piece of equipment for a beekeeper with a few hives. This consists of a well insulated box, ideally with a double-glazed cover, facing the sun. Inside, a metal tray delivers the melted wax through a coarse sieve into a removable metal container.

A well designed solar wax extractor and a nice sunny day can recover up to 80% of the wax in brood combs and more from cappings. It is useful if the tray is big enough to take a few brood frames.

The solar wax extractor is placed outside in the sun from April to September and brought into a shed or covered for protection against the weather over the winter months.

Mine is mounted on an old sack barrow so I can turn it to face the sun during the day. On a good day the temperature in the box can reach 70 to 90°C. Beeswax melts at 62 to 64°C. One advantage of this method is that some bleaching of the wax occurs in sunlight and another is that there is no energy cost involved.

You can place bits of wax directly into the extractor throughout the summer, as and when you collect it. I found that quite early in the season the extractor became clogged with debris and the process became rather messy. For this reason I prefer to collect all the brace comb and other bits of wax and, after washing in rain water to remove all traces of honey, place them into a muslin bag or the legs of old tights. One half of a leg is long enough!

A solar wax extractor mounted on a sack barrow. It is half loaded with cappings in tights

On a really nice sunny day I fill the extractor with these packages and quite clean melted wax is delivered to the tray. The debris is filtered out by the tights; some wax is also retained in the debris and cocoons in the residue.

Blocks of wax produced by any of these methods should be clean enough to be acceptable for exchange for foundation by equipment suppliers. If you wish to use the wax to enter a competition or to make candles or polish, it needs to be melted again and filtered.

The residue, known as slumgum, still contains some beeswax and this can be recovered commercially by using a steam jacketed wax press. For most beekeepers the tights and slumgum make good firelighters!

Making use of beeswax

One way to make good use of the recovered wax is by simply exchanging it for foundation from the equipment suppliers. The wax straight from the steamer or the solar wax extractor is quite acceptable for exchange without any further melting and filtering. After making some beeswax products such as candles and polish, I now prefer to exchange most of my beeswax for foundation.

It is necessary to filter the wax through a fine cloth before you use it for making candles or other products. I used a double saucepan to melt the wax and immersed into the molten wax a suitable sized sieve covered on the outside with lint. The filtered wax inside the sieve could be lifted out using a small ladle.

Our local group of beekeepers once gathered together our recovered wax and spent a Saturday making our own foundation. It was a sociable and instructive activity and well worth while. However, the home-made foundation turned out to be rather brittle so quite a lot was broken as I placed it in the frames. Perhaps if we had persevered we could have overcome this disadvantage.

Small clean 50 g blocks of beeswax are useful for easing wooden drawers on their runners or zips and other uses. They can be produced very simply by pouring melted beeswax into moulds after they have been polished by washing up liquid, so that the set block of beeswax will not stick to the mould. Various designs of moulds are available from equipment suppliers.

Beeswax candles make very attractive gifts and can decorate your table during Christmas festivities. It is a straightforward process to make moulded candles using silicone moulds.

Beeswax candles. Evidence of beeswax
candles is found in Egyptian tombs 3,100
to 3,500 years ago

You can make a simple furniture polish by stirring about
100 g of shredded beeswax into 250 ml of pure turpentine and
letting the mixture set. Other kinds of polish and creams can be
produced by adding other types of wax or soap flakes. Recipes
are available in books and the internet. Pure turpentine, available
from the equipment suppliers, is a hazardous and very flammable
substance, so be very careful to follow the safety warnings on
the label.

20 THE NEXT STEPS

Following reflection on your beekeeping during the past year, decide what you want to do about those aspects you consider could be improved. Perhaps you can get help from books, the internet, a discussion with an experienced beekeeper or a winter meeting of your local group.

What are your next steps in beekeeping? What is your plan for the year? Do you want to keep the same number of hives or will you expand? Work out your plan and prepare by getting the extra equipment during the winter, when you can often get good offers from suppliers. Include in your plan time to learn about some more advanced beekeeping skills. Here are some ideas for next spring.

Marking and clipping the queen's wing

Having a marked queen in your hive makes her much easier to find when necessary, such as when the colony is making swarming preparations or you want to unite colonies or re-queen. The best time to mark your queen is in early spring when she is more easily found among a small number of bees. Once you have learnt to mark the queen it is only a small step to clip one of her wings. This too can help with swarm control.

I suggest that you use the marking pen sold by beekeeping equipment suppliers. It is convenient to use and you can be sure that it is safe. First of all check the queen marking pen by marking a spot on anything, to make sure the paint does not flood out. This will help you to avoid clogging the queen's spiracles, her breathing tubes, or covering parts of her antennae with paint.

Choose a fine day in early spring with no breeze. There will be only three or four frames with brood and far fewer bees than you would find when the bees decide to swarm.

Press-in marking cage

At first you may prefer to use a press-in queen marking cage available from the equipment suppliers. You will be able to mark the queen without picking her up. Place the hive roof upside down nearby on a stand about waist high if possible to be kind to your back, or on the ground. When you see the queen, place the frame in the upturned roof, keeping an eye on the queen.

Press-in cage. Care is needed to avoid 'spearing' the queen

As soon as your hands are free, pick up the press-in queen marking cage and place it very carefully over the queen. Gently press the spikes into the comb. Continue pressing until the queen is just held between the comb and the cross threads of the cage. Try to get the queen trapped with her thorax framed by the threads. It does not matter if some worker bees may be caught inside the cage with the queen. They can get out between the spikes if they wish.

Now you can mark the queen's thorax with the marking pen. Release the cage a little but keep the queen trapped for about 30 seconds to allow the paint to dry, before lifting the cage clear. There is an internationally agreed colour code for queen marking. Years ending 1 and 6 are white, 2 and 7 are yellow, 3 and 8 red, 4 and 9 green and 5 and 0 blue. Not only is it easier to spot the queen, you will know her age and if she has been superseded. Of course you can use any colour that stands out best for you if you prefer.

It may be worth while practising using the press-in cage on drones or workers before you attempt to mark the queen. Trapping her in the cage without spearing her with the spikes needs a bit of skill and good timing. When this happened to me I decided to practise picking up the queen instead!

Picking up the queen

Another advantage of picking up the queen is that you can clip her wing at the same time as marking her. You can also clip her wing when she is trapped in a queen marking cage but care is needed not to cut the cross threads on the cage.

This is how I pick up the queen. When I see her I simply pick her up by the wings or thorax using the thumb and first finger of my right hand. I then transfer her to my left hand holding her by the thorax between the thumb and first finger and letting her stand on my second finger. Now I use the pen to place a small spot of coloured paint on her thorax. I then place the marked queen in a cage or matchbox and allow the paint to dry before I return her to the colony.

Some hold the queen by the legs. The queen's thorax, wings and legs are surprisingly robust but you should never hold her by the abdomen, which is swollen with precious eggs. If you prefer to wear gloves you may find it useful to guide the queen into a clip-type queen cage then take her to a bee-free area. Then take off your gloves so that you handle the queen with clean, propolis-free hands. If you have been unable to find the queen yet, for example to carry out a swarm control procedure, I suggest that you practise picking up and handling drones at any time during the summer. During the following spring you can learn to find and mark the queen.

Marking the queen. The queen is held by the thorax

Geoff Close

Clipping the queen's wing

Clipping the queen's wing simply means cutting off about one half of the pair of wings on one side to prevent the queen flying. There are no nerve endings in the wings so it does not hurt the queen. It's like cutting your hair or finger nails.

I use small fine scissors in my right hand and hold the queen by the thorax in the left hand. I steady the scissors on my left thumb, slowly work one pair of wings into the scissors, watch out to avoid trapping a leg as the queen attempts to push the scissors to one side, then clip half of one pair of wings. If you are left-handed the scissors are held in the left hand and the queen in the right. Then proceed straight away to mark the queen.

An unclipped queen will usually fly out with a swarm after the first queen cell is sealed, that is eight days after the egg was laid. A clipped queen however will be reluctant to leave and when she does will fall to the ground. Occasionally the bees will cluster around the queen on the ground but usually they realise the queen is lost only when they consolidate on a nearby tree and the bees return to the hive. The queen is lost but the bees are in the hive. They will undoubtedly swarm out again when the first virgin has emerged, 16 or so days after the egg was laid. These timings may be reduced because worker bees sometimes carry eggs from a worker cell into a queen cell and also convert a worker cell into an 'emergency' queen cell starting with a two-day-old or even a four-day-old larva. Having a clipped queen in the colony gives the beekeeper more time between seeing queen cells with fed larvae and the

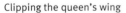
Clipping the queen's wing

Geoff Close

swarm leaving. Some will extend the regular inspections from seven to 10 days.

I have clipped my queens in the early spring for many years and I still carry out my regular inspections every seven days; occasionally I appreciate the extra few days available when for some reason the planned inspection has to give way to something even more important. The main benefit I have found is that I do not lose a swarm even if I lose the queen. The clipped queen attempting to fly out with a swarm will fall into the grass and when the bees gather on a nearby tree and discover they have no queen, they return to the hive. Another advantage is that there are fewer swarms settling in neighbours' gardens and property causing nuisance and concern.

You can hold the queen by her legs. Make sure you have two or three legs trapped

Geoff Close

Making a nucleus

I would encourage you to learn to make up a nucleus, usually called a 'nuc', as soon as you can. A nuc is very useful for a hobby beekeeper as well as for a large scale enterprise.

Making up a nuc from a strong colony can help delay swarming preparations by reducing the population of bees and brood. If a colony has started preparations for swarming you can make two or sometimes three nucs, each with a queen cell, to increase your stocks. An even better approach is to introduce a mature queen cell from a 'selected' colony showing good characteristics. However, you should never let a nuc raise its own queen from an egg or young larva. The result will be an undersize 'scrub' queen because the small population will not be able to nurture the larva as can a full-sized colony.

Introducing a new queen to a strong colony any time from May to mid August is more likely to succeed when the queen is first introduced to a nuc. I never attempt to introduce a queen to a colony during the summer without first making a two frame nuc to receive the queen for the first week.

A nuc is made up of two or three frames initially in a box that will accommodate four or five frames with bees, brood and a queen or queen cell. The frames of brood and bees can be taken from a single colony or from two or three colonies. Unless you have an out-apiary you will probably want to keep the nuc in the same apiary as the 'mother' colony providing the bees and brood. By stocking the nuc with younger workers and delaying opening the entrance you reduce the number of bees immediately flying back to

A National nucleus hive. The roof will accommodate a small round feeder

their original site. You can reduce the risk of the little colony being robbed out by delaying additional feeding for about four days.

Here is the method I use to make up a nuc to stay in the same apiary as the mother colony:

- find the queen in the strong healthy mother colony that will provide the bees for your nuc and place the frame with the queen in a temporary box, or place her in a cage with three or four workers for safe keeping
- select two or three frames with mostly emerging brood and lightly shake the frames over the hive to lose the older flying bees. Place the frames with emerging brood and young bees in the nuc box
- now add more young bees from two or three frames by giving each frame a light shake over the brood chamber to remove the older bees, then a more vigorous shake into the nuc box to dislodge the young bees. It is essential to have plenty of adults in your nuc to care for the brood
- check that there is some food on the frames of emerging brood and add a frame with mainly food, and fill the nuc box with drawn comb or foundation
- lightly block the entrance of the nuc with grass to settle the bees in the nuc
- provide additional food if needed after four days
- introduce the mature or virgin queen or queen cell as you wish after making sure that there are no started queen cells in the nuc

- replace the frame and queen into the mother colony and add frames of drawn comb or foundation at the sides to fill up the brood box.

If you are moving the nuc more than three miles away from the mother colony, all the flying bees will now stay in the nuc. You can simply take two frames of emerging brood and one with food, all with adhering bees, and shake in all the bees from an additional frame.

Other uses for a nuc include holding and extending the life of a queen you have chosen for raising queen cells, queen mating, drawing out worker comb and maintaining an observation hive. Why not add this to your list of areas to start studying now? Prepare by making or buying the necessary equipment in time for next season.

Simple selective queen rearing

Many beekeepers with only a few hives rely on splitting swarmed stocks to raise new queens, to replace queens or increase stocks. Beekeepers who regularly make up nucs often add queen cells from swarming colonies. The result may be that these queens are selected from colonies showing a strong swarming characteristic. Most of us would include a low inclination to swarm as one of the desirable characteristics for our bees.

Importing a mature queen cell

Experienced beekeepers with a dozen or more hives can select a 'best' colony with desirable attributes. The beginner with only one or two colonies can make a start with selective queen raising by importing a selected mature queen cell from a local experienced beekeeper who rears queens. Improving the quality of bees in a locality benefits all beekeepers in the area, so beekeepers that raise their own queens will usually be pleased to provide queen cells from their selected stock for small scale beekeepers to introduce into their nucs. Perhaps there may be a nominal charge of a few pounds, considerably less than buying in a new queen with the risk of loss during introduction.

First of all discuss with the queen-raiser how you will make up a nuc and the date when the queen cell will be ready to be transferred to the mating nuc. This will be one or two days before the queen is due to emerge, so the transfer must be done on the appointed day come rain or shine.

Prepare the mating nuc seven days before the transfer day so that the bees cannot make their own queen cells when you introduce your selected queen cell. Then:

- on the transfer day remove any queen cells that may have been started in the nuc before you collect the queen cell
- collect the queen cell and transport it carefully maintaining its temperature at about 35°C. Keep it vertical, for example in a matchbox in your breast pocket
- place the queen cell vertically on the comb near brood so that when the queen emerges she will be where the bees would expect to find her
- after two or three days you can examine the queen cell to check that the queen has emerged. You can expect the queen to be mated and start laying in two to three weeks.

Introducing a queen cell. The queen will emerge on to brood, where the bees expect to find her

Geoff Close

Rearing a queen from your own colony

When you have built up to three or more colonies it will be worth while raising your own queens, including producing your own queen cells from your best colony. Here is a method to rear three or four queens.

The best queens are raised from eggs or very young larvae less than 24 hours old in a large colony with plenty of nurse bees well fed on pollen and honey or sugar syrup.

You should select the breeder colony that shows your desired characteristics. This is the colony whose queen will provide the eggs or young larvae. Most beekeepers would look for a good-tempered colony whose bees do not run around all over the comb when you examine them and are not inclined to swarm readily. Also the colony should of course be healthy and productive.

The cell-building colony will produce the queen cells and nourish the selected larvae. Select your strongest colony early in the spring to be your cell builder and add a second brood box T with frames of drawn comb or foundation instead of the queen excluder and super. Feed if using foundation. The cell builder may also be the breeder colony providing the eggs or larvae. If available take out and keep to one side a frame of mainly pollen from any colony that may have surplus supplies during the spring.

Start your queen-raising procedure so that there will be drones available to mate with the queen, and ideally when you expect a good spell of fine weather. This usually means Day 0 is around mid to late May.

Day 0

- in the cell builder sort the frames with all the open brood into the upper box T. Add a frame of mainly pollen if available into the middle of T. Fill with frames of sealed brood. Sort the remaining sealed brood, queen and other frames into the bottom box B
- shake all the bees into B. Add a queen excluder between B, with all the bees, queen and sealed brood, and T, with mainly open brood and no bees. Feed sugar syrup. The nurse bees will migrate to T and the queen will continue to lay in B. After seven days most of the brood in T will be sealed and too old to start queen cells.

Day 7

- move the bottom box B and floor to one side and now place the upper box T on a new floor on the original site. In box T examine the frames and remove any queen cells that may have been started. Remove one empty frame and add a frame with eggs from the breeder colony into Box T. Place the frame of eggs next to the frame of pollen if available. Feed sugar syrup

- in box B check that the queen is laying and that there are plenty of bees, and frames with emerging brood. The flying bees will go back to the original site and join the cell-building colony.

Day 11
- in the cell-builder T, examine the breeder frame for queen cells and remove any that are sealed, leaving only open queen cells. This will mean that the remaining queen cells have been started from larvae less than 24 hours old or from eggs. Check that there are plenty of bees in B.

Day 17
- prepare two or three nucs from the cell builder in T. Each may need a frame of stores. Introduce one queen cell to each nuc using the frame with a queen cell for one. Keep the queen cell vertical and avoid putting any pressure on the cell. Press the wax supporting the queen cell into the comb so that the queen emerges on to brood. Close the entrance and place the nucs in a cool dark place for two days and place on their site in the apiary at dusk
- move box B back to its original site, add a queen excluder and add supers as needed to continue as a honey producing colony.

Day 19/20
- queens have emerged.

Day 24/25
- queens are ready to mate.

Day 26/40
- queens should start laying.

Shook Swarm

Part of the treatment recommended by the NBU for EFB is to shake the entire colony on to new foundation and to destroy the old combs. This eliminates all the disease spores which build up in the combs in one operation and reduces the risk of the disease recurring. It has also been found that a colony treated in this way thrives with new vigour and develops quickly into a strong colony. The same procedure, known as a 'shook swarm', can be effective to deal with a serious outbreak of the more common brood diseases, nosema and chalk brood.

It can be used too as a preventative measure to eliminate the load of pathogens building up in the brood combs and so reduce the risk of brood diseases developing. When the shook swarm is carried out early in the season the colony usually thrives and develops into a strong productive colony, making up for the loss of the initial brood and perhaps some food stores. The lost brood may also include a batch of varroa mites being raised.

You can carry out this procedure on a strong colony with four or five frames with brood. If this is done early in the season, say up to mid April, the new bees will become foragers in time for the spring nectar flow; otherwise you may miss the spring crop.

Here is the procedure, step by step:

- prepare a sterilised brood box with a full complement of frames with foundation, floor, crownboard and queen excluder
- move the hive including floor, with the colony you intend to transfer on to new foundation, to one side leaving the hive stand on the original site
- place the clean floor on the hive stand with the entrance facing the same way as in the original hive. Then place the queen excluder on the floor and the brood box with frames of foundation on top of the queen excluder. Foragers will soon be returning. The queen excluder below the brood box will prevent the brood-less colony absconding
- find and cage the queen and keep her in a safe place. There is a risk of losing the queen if she is simply shaken into the box with the bees
- remove some of the centre frames of foundation. Shake and if necessary brush all the bees from the original hive into the clean brood box. Replace the frames of foundation
- release the queen into the new brood box when you have completed the transfer of all the bees
- replace the crownboard and feed with sugar syrup until all the foundation is drawn out. Insert the varroa mite monitoring tray in the open mesh floor to help the bees maintain a higher temperature for comb-building
- remove the queen excluder when there is new brood present, usually after about a week.

How you deal with the old combs depends on why you transferred the colony on to new foundation. If it was part of the treatment for EFB, confirmed and recommended by a bee inspector, the old combs should be wrapped in old paper and burned straight away. Also, if you used the shook swarm procedure to deal with a serious outbreak of nosema or chalk brood good practice is to destroy the infected comb.

When you use the shook swarm procedure to inhibit the development of brood diseases, perhaps on a two- or three-year cycle, there may be a few combs in quite good condition in the old brood box. Frames with combs in good condition may be cleaned and sterilised using acetic acid and used again. The wax can be recovered from other combs and the cleaned and sterilised frames fitted with new foundation.

Basic test of your competence

When you have completed your first full year of beekeeping you should have achieved a basic level of competence. All the beekeeping associations in the British Isles organise voluntary assessments to check that you are able to care for a colony of honey bees safely. Surely every beekeeper would want to know that they have achieved this basic level of competence. Most people taking the assessment say they enjoyed the experience even if they were a bit apprehensive at first. It is usually a good learning opportunity as well.

I suggest that you find out the entry requirements and entry form by contacting your association. Also get a copy of the syllabus so that you can be sure that you have studied all the likely topics that may crop up. After you have passed the basic test or assessment you can go on to study beekeeping in greater depth and enjoy your hobby even more.

APPENDIX 1

EQUIPMENT NEEDED TO START BEEKEEPING

The following list is the equipment needed to start beekeeping with one colony and to care for the bees during the first year. Hives are available assembled or as flat packs. Second-hand equipment should always be sterilised by scorching with a blow lamp. Do not use any second-hand drawn comb.

Personal equipment
- Hat/veil to protect the face, eyes, mouth, nose, ears
- Overalls (with zips), made of smooth, light-coloured material
- Hive tool
- Smoker (large size)
- Gloves ('Marigold' or similar kitchen gloves)
- Wellingtons or some other protection for the ankles

National or Smith hive (for WBC hives add 5 lifts to the following list)
- Open mesh floor with varroa monitoring screen and entrance block
- Brood chamber
- Frames (Hoffman DN5 frames, 27 mm wide bars)*
- BS deep wired foundation*
- Queen excluder (framed wire type)
- 3 Supers
- Frames for the supers*
- BS shallow wired beeswax foundation*
- Pack of wide (50 mm) and narrow (37 mm) plastic frame spacers in supers
- Crownboard
- Roof

Reserve hive for swarm control
- Open mesh floor with varroa monitoring screen snd entrance block
- Brood chamber
- Frames (Hoffman DN5, 27 mm wide bars)*
- BS deep wired foundation*
- Crownboard
- Roof

Other equipment
- Crownboard for clearing supers
- 2 Porter bee escapes
- Round plastic rapid feeder, or contact feeder
- Uncapping fork (for harvesting honey)
- Hive stand (to allow air circulation all round the hive)

* Frames and foundation are usually supplied in packs of 10 or 50.

APPENDIX 2

COLONY RECORD

I find it helpful to use numbers for most of the conditions that need to be recorded. Abbreviated words or shorthand are used for items that are not routinely recorded.

Some conditions such as 'gentleness' and 'quiet' are marked 1 to 4, the high number consistently reflecting 'good' and low number 'poor'.

After a little practice I can recall and enter all the items on the record card after completing the colony examination. Using numbers also makes it is easier to search the record, for example to find a candidate breeder queen. I suggest that you develop your own method that works best for you.

Notes:
Occupied frames (*The number of frames in the brood box occupied by bees*)
Frames brood (*The number of frames with brood*)
Brood stages (*E for eggs, L larvae, S sealed brood, or a tick if all stages*)
Brood area (*4 for one frame full of brood on one side, 3 for ¾ full, 2 for ½, 1 for ¼ or less*)
Brood pattern (*4 for good, 3 for acceptable, 2 for poor and 1 for unacceptable*)
Stores (*4 for more than 4 Kg, 1 for need feeding immediately*)
Gentle (*4 for excellent to 1 for unacceptable*)
Quiet on comb (*4 for good to 1 for poor*)
Q seen (*Ref no or colour, or tick if not marked, c if clipped*)
Queen cells (*o for open, s for sealed, number of queen cells found*)
Weather (*4 for calm sunny and warm, to 1 for poor*)
Remarks (*abbreviated text covering health, treatment for disease, beekeeper's actions, additions and subtractions such as supers, frames*)

Apiary:												Hive:		Queen:
Date	Occupied frames	Frames brood	E/L/S	Area	Pattern	Gentle	Quiet	Q seen & ref	Q cells o/s no	Food	Weather	Remarks	Health	Actions

APPENDIX 3

REFERENCES AND FURTHER READING

Books

Cook, V. (1986) *Queen rearing simplified*. Geddington, British Bee Publications Ltd.

Dade, H. A. (1962) *Anatomy and Dissection of the Honeybee*. London, IBRA.

Davis, C. F. (2004) *The Honey Bee Inside Out*. Stoneleigh, Bee Craft Limited.

Davis, C. F. (2007) *The Honey Bee Around and About*. Stoneleigh, Bee Craft Limited.

de Bruyn, C. (1997) *Practical Beekeeping*. Marlborough, The Crowood Press.

Hooper, T. (1976) *Guide to Bees and Honey*. 4th edition 2005. Poole, Blandford Press Ltd.

Hooper, T.; Taylor, M. (1988) *The Beekeeper's Garden*. Sherborne, Alphabooks Ltd.

Howes, F. N. (1979) *Plants and Beekeeping*. 2nd edition. London, Faber and Faber Limited.

Kirk, W. D. J. (1994) *A colour guide to the pollen loads of the honey bee*. Cardiff, IBRA.

Morse, R.; Hooper, T. (eds.) (1985) *The Illustrated Encyclopedia of Beekeeping*. Poole, Blandford Press.

Riches, H. (1997) *Mead Making, Exhibiting and Judging*. Charlestown, Bee Books New & Old.

Seely, T. D. (1995) *The Wisdom of the Hive*. Cambridge, MA, Harvard University Press.

Waring, A.; C. (2006) *Teach Yourself Beekeeping*. London. Hodder Education.

Winston, M. L. (1987) *The Biology of the Honey Bee*. Cambridge, MA, Harvard University Press.

Disease recognition

Bee Disease Recognition Guide. A set of four laminated apiary guides describing with photographs healthy brood and particular diseases, available from Bee Craft Limited.

The following four publications describe the biology, effect, signs and treatment of the diseases. They are published by The Department for Environment, Food and Rural Affairs (DEFRA) and are available from the National Bee Unit (NBU).

Foul Brood Disease of Honey Bees; recognition and control
Managing Varroa
The Small Hive Beetle
Tropilaelaps: parasitic mites of honey bees

Parasites of the Honey Bee. Produced by Dr Mary F Coffey. Teagasc, Crops Research Centre, Oak Park, Carlow, Republic of Ireland.

INDEX